# THE PRINTED MAPS

## of

## EXETER

## 1587 – 1901

### *300 Years of Exeter History*

**Francis  Bennett**

**& Kit Batten**

*With an Introduction by Dick Passmore*

# THE PRINTED MAPS

## of

## EXETER

## 1587 – 1901

### *300 Years of Exeter History*

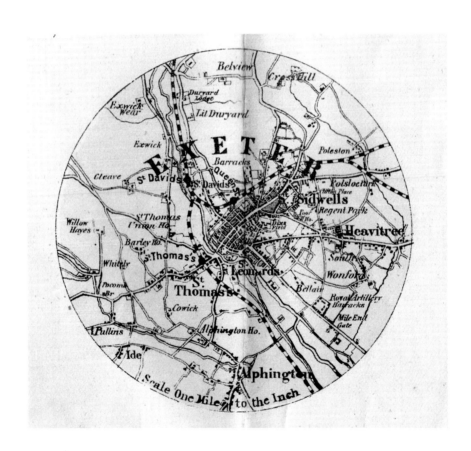

**Francis Bennett**

**& Kit Batten**

*With an Introduction by Dick Passmore*

*The Printed Maps of Exeter*
*1587 – 1901*
*300 Years of Exeter History*

**First Published in Great Britain in 2011 by Little Silver Publications.**

**ISBN 0 – 9544472 – 6 – 7**

**Published on behalf of the authors by**
**Little Silver Publications**
**Little Silver Cottage**
**Little Silver Lane**
**Matford**
**Exeter EX2 8XZ**
**Devon**

**This book has been made possible by the kind cooperation of the Westcountry Studies Library in Exeter, part of Devon Libraries.**

Printed by The Short Run Press Ltd, 25 Bittern Road, Exeter  EX2 7LW.

# Contents

## The Printed Maps of Exeter

## 1587 – 1901

## 300 Years of Exeter History

| Contents | Page |
|---|---|
| Foreword by Anne Howard | 7 |
| Acknowledgements | 8 |
| A Brief History of Exeter by Dick Passmore | 9 |
| The Printed Maps of Exeter – Catalogue | 21 |
| Select Bibliography of Books on Devon Maps | 101 |
| Appendix A – John Hooker States and Derivatives | 102 |
| Appendix B – John Richards | 103 |
| Appendix C – Henry Besley | 104 |
| Index | 107 |

# Foreword

The authors of this present work are both keen collectors of Devon maps and have been compiling cartobibliographies, or lists of maps, of the county for a number of years. In 1996 and 2000 they published two books listing all the printed maps of the complete county which appeared between 1575, when the first printed map of the county was engraved and printed, and 1901 when Queen Victoria died. They have been interested in the mapping of Exeter for a number of years and this present volume catalogues the wealth of map material contained in historical surveys, guide books or published as folding maps showing the development of Exeter from the time of John Hooker up until the death of Queen Victoria. The aim has been to include every printed map of Exeter published on one sheet in the period up to 1901. The maps catalogued here mean that every Exonian interested in mapping of any sort should find something of interest. These 62 maps include the first printed map by John Hooker of 1587 plus two other maps executed by him but not actually printed until the 1890s. There are early plans attempting to show how the city looked even before Hooker's time and plans of the castle and precincts. Each map is described and illustrated and an attempt has been made to put it in its historical context.

As a librarian new to the collections of maps held in the Westcountry Studies Library the information and detail contained in this book will prove invaluable.

Anne Howard
Local Studies Librarian
Westcountry Studies Library
Exeter

West View of the GREAT CONDUIT at Carfoix, taken down 1770.

**The Great Conduit stood from 1441 to 1770 (see Jenkins, 17)**

# Acknowledgements

Although there are numerous books on Exeter, to paraphrase the words of D'Urban and Mathew writing over a hundred years ago: *Although a work on the* [Maps of Exeter] *has already been issued ... , it did not seem so thoroughly to exhaust the subject as to exclude another which should deal more fully with the numerous points of interest in the* [County of Exeter].[1]

We would like to thank Anne Howard, Local Studies Librarian, of the Westcountry Studies Library in Exeter for her Foreword and are also highly delighted to have Dick Passmore, author of *The Story of the Theatre Royal Exeter,* write an introduction covering some of Exeter□s history. He has been actively interested in the history of Exeter for many years and kindly agreed to write a brief overview on the city and its growth over 300 years.

We would like to thank the Westcountry Studies Library in Exeter for their help and assistance, without which this book could not have been written. They have given their time and provided illustrations on so many occasions. This book is really dedicated to the all staff of the library.

5, 7, 8*, 10*, 11*, 12, 13, 15*, 27, 30*, 37*, 38, 40, 43, 44, 45, 51* and 63* are reproduced by kind permission of the Exeter Westcountry Studies Library. Our thanks go to Katherine Dunhill of WSL for scanning (*).

1, 22 and 23 are reproduced by kind permission of Devon Record Office, our thanks to John Draisey for his assistance.

29 is reproduced by kind permission of the Devon & Exeter Institute. Our thanks to Charles Fleming for taking the photograph.

All photographs of 47 are reproduced by kind permission of Malcolm Woodward.

All other illustrations are taken from maps in possession of the authors.

Cover illustrations: the county map of Devon by John Speed (entry 2) with inset plan of Exeter taken from a copy published from approximately 1623 to 1665 by John Sudbury and George Humble (front); the plan of Exeter executed by Ichabod Fairlove (entry 8) and engraved by Joseph Coles in 1709 (back).

The *Printed Maps of Devonshire 1575 – 1837* appeared in 1996 and listed the first 117 county maps of Devon to be printed. The continuation, *The Victorian Maps of Devon 1838 – 1901,* was published in 2000 and listed maps 118 – 182. Where reference is made to these maps in the text the relevant county maps will be noted as **B&B** followed by the particular catalogue number. Copies of the up-to-date versions of these two books can be ordered from the authors.

Numbers in brackets refer to maps in this cartobibliography.

December 2010

Francis Bennett
Menryn, Court Wood
Newton Ferrers PL8 1BW
England

Kit Batten
Auerhahnweg 7
70499 Stuttgart
Germany

---

[1] D'Urban and Mathew; *The Birds of Devon*; published by R H Porter of London; 1892.

# A Brief History of Exeter

## By Dick Passmore

EXETER, the county town of Devon, is one of the oldest cities in England, and able to boast of settlements prior to the Roman invasion of our country, possibly two hundred years before. Iron age settlements have been excavated recently in various areas of the city, although these settlements appear to have been small, possibly just farms, rather than the remains of anything larger. Certainly a Roman legionary fortress was set up in c.55 – 60 AD, lasting until c.75 AD. Recently evidence of further Roman military activity around Exeter has been found, possibly pre-dating the fortress by a few years – but archaeological work on this aspect continues, and at present has to be classed as possible, rather than definite. The early Roman civil town of Exeter was established around 80 AD on the site of the earlier fortress, and was enclosed by a solid wall several years later, in the second century. Much of that original wall still exists today, although parts have been restored and other parts removed for modern-day improvements to the city. W T P Shortt attempted to plot the Roman town of Exeter (see 28) but the plan is largely speculation based on the finds of coins. When the Romans left Exeter, early in the fifth century, the city doubtless took on a different mantle, but little is known of the next three hundred years.

## Early occupation

The Anglo-Saxons occupied Exeter during the 7th century and an Abbey was built, approximately on the site of the existing Cathedral. Then followed the Danes, who took the city in 876, but were dismissed from Exeter by King Alfred only to return about one hundred and fifty years later! They were at first repelled, but, led by King Sweyn, later gained access to the city and plundered it, setting buildings alight and destroying the Abbey. They left the city in virtual ruin, and never returned. The Normans took over England in 1066, and shortly afterwards found Exeter, already a busy town, with almost five hundred houses and a population of some 2,500. The occupation of Exeter by the Normans saw the rebuilding of the Abbey – probably one of the highlights of Exeter's history, for it was the Normans who started to create what is now the magnificent Cathedral of St. Peter, set in the centre of the city. The twin towers of today's Cathedral are indeed of Norman origin.

## The Castle

George Oliver in *The History of the City of Exeter* devoted a chapter to the origins of the castle and walls which he attributed to King Athelstan at some time between 925 and 941 giving the outline traced by Kerslake (see 46). Despite extensive destruction by Sweyn, as mentioned above, the city rose again under the support of Canute and Edward the Confessor so that by the time of the conquest Exeter had gained city proportions. However, the castle is not documented in the Domesday Survey of 1086 and was possibly only completed some time later. The gateway certainly leads one to suspect completion during, or shortly after, Norman architectural influence.

John Leland is reputed to have visited Exeter in 1542 on his extensive travels and a manuscript plan of the castle dating back to the 16th century is extant (35). However, although long credited to Leland himself, the manuscript plan in the British Library may be a later speculation of what Leland saw, produced some years after his death (in 1552).

Norden (36), who surveyed the castle in 1617, gives us the most detailed description of the castle. He shows the sally port in the extreme North East corner, and a tower between the entrance gate and the South East corner, but omits the bastion clearly shown by others (e.g. manuscript maps of 1600 or the manuscript maps of Hooker) between the entrance gate and the north west (i.e. Athelstan's) tower. However, the castle shown on one of Hooker's drawings of St. Sidwell's fee (see 61) clearly shows both the bastion and Norden's tower.

However it is safe to assume that at some time both existed. The plan in Jenkin' *History of Exeter* in 1806 (18), based on the so-called Leland plan, moves the sally port back towards the sessions house in the centre and shows both bastions (but not the tower between the gate and the south east corner). In an article in 1912 C B Lyster, writing about the city walls (*Devon & Cornwall, Notes & Queries Vol. VII*), noted that there were archaeological finds that showed the foundations of both. One is left with the supposition that the south bastion was so ruined by the beginning of the seventeenth century that Norden did not consider it worth drawing.

## Parishes

Frederic Kelly's *Directory of Devonshire* (e.g. 1893, p.171) mentions that in 1222, Exeter had 19 churches, two of which (St. Sidwell's and St. David's) "stood without the walls". White's *Directory of Devonshire* for 1850 states that prior to 1658 Exeter had 32 churches (probably including the suburbs and non-conformists), although 12 had been sold in that year (p.81). The same directory states that in 1850 the city and suburbs had no less than 21 parish churches and several episcopal chapels. It was during the thirteenth century that parishes first appeared in Exeter, although there had been many churches constructed during earlier centuries, none had defined areas, or parishes as we now know them. The newly created parishes tended to follow the lines of streets and lanes, and people resident within those areas would attend the church within that parish, each parish having its own priest. Although some of the parishes disappeared long ago, early maps of Exeter show the names of parishes within the city. It was not until 1956 that parish boundaries were revised, some being amalgamated with adjoining parishes, with priests looking after the spiritual needs of two, three or perhaps four parishes. That system still exists today.

## Growth of the city

During the thirteenth and fourteenth centuries Exeter started to grow, and records show various taverns, houses, shops and other buildings springing up, making the city a busy place in which to live and work. Taverns, it has to be said, were of considerable importance in those days. Not only were they ale-houses – and thus of social importance, they were also meeting places, and places of entertainment. They were also a useful means of providing an address; when Hermann Moll's *Fifty-Six New and Acurate Maps* was published in 1708 it was printed by John Nicholson at the Kings-Arms, John Sprint at the Bell in Little-Britain and Andrew Bell at the Cross-Keys and Bible in London, for example. In Exeter the Seven Stars inn also served as one of the city's earliest theatres, and is thought to have hosted John Gay's *The Beggars Opera* in 1728 as the first performance outside London. The city was filling up within the old walls, and space was becoming valuable.
The end of the 12th century also saw one of the most important additions to Exeter – the underground water supply. Until then, citizens would collect their own water from the Exe, or pay water-bearers who would carry pails of water on yokes throughout the city, selling the water from the River Exe to houses and businesses. The introduction of piped water was of significant importance to the city, although Minchinton (1987) states that water bearers were still existent in the early 19th century. The underground system commenced with the tapping of a spring in the higher part of the parish of St. Sidwell, owned by the Dean and Chapter. They were the first to take advantage of the new system, and were able to supply the Cathedral with fresh water. The water was brought underground into the Cathedral Close where it terminated in the newly-built St. Peter's Conduit. A further supply was taken to Fore Street, to serve St. Nicholas' Priory. However, more importantly, in 1346 an agreement was made whereby the water from St. Peter's Conduit could be taken to another new conduit in South Street. This was later demolished and in 1441 the new Great Conduit was constructed at The Carfax - the junction of High Street, Fore Street, South Street and North Street. The conduit stood until the late eighteenth century, having supplied Exeter with water for over three hundred years. The Great Conduit can clearly be seen on various maps, including those of Hooker (1), Speed (2), Braun & Hogenberg (3) and Izacke (7) and is reference 6 on Nicholls' plan (page 12). Today, Exeter's "underground passages", as they are now named, are in fact the narrow, low tunnels constructed to carry water from St. Sidwell's, open to the public where visitors can see a small section of the original passages and pipework. It must be said, however, that they are not suitable for those who suffer from claustrophobia.
From the Roman days, when it was a walled city, Exeter and its population have both grown century by century, until Exeter is now a city of some 125,000 people, taking up an area of several square miles. Being walled, the city was somewhat insular (as were many other cities and towns), and although the walls were designed to protect the city, on more than one occasion those walls have been breached and the city invaded – notably by the Danes c.876, and William the Conqueror in 1068. In 1496 Perkin Warbeck attempted to take the city, but was repelled. Henry VII visited the city shortly afterwards and presented it with a Sword and Cap of Maintenance as a gift, in gratitude for the city's loyalty to the Crown. Both the Sword and Cap are retained to this day as part of the city's Regalia. In 1549 Hooker witnessed the siege during the Prayer Book Rebellion. During the English Civil War, Exeter was besieged and taken over by the Royalists in 1643 only to be surrendered to General Fairfax in 1646. Since then the city has been free of any form of siege, although it was, of course, seriously affected by German bombing raids in 1942, as will be seen later.

## Exeter documented

Exeter has been inhabited for over two thousand years, and the main thoroughfare, High Street, has been in continuous use during that period, and was originally one of several ridgeways around the city. The story of Exeter is therefore of great interest to historians, and has been documented since at least the 15th century (and possibly earlier), by way of manuscripts, books and maps. Certainly John Hooker's numerous writings such as his *Catalogue of Bishops* in 1584 and his other works, many only extant as manuscripts, of around that time are amongst the earliest and provide us with a good perspective on life in Exeter at that time. Almost a century later Richard Izacke wrote his *Antiquities of the City of Exeter* - a book now sought by collectors - and which provides the modern reader with a catalogue of events, both major and trivial, but which nonetheless give us a vivid impression of life at that time. His son's continuation is also a valuable contribution to Exeter's historical writings.

While later writers tried to imagine what Exeter looked like before the Middle Ages (e.g. Kerslake or Freeman) the earliest contemporary maps of Exeter, for example Hooker's map of 1587 (1), depict the walled city on the north bank of the River Exe, with just a few outlying settlements, and those being mainly agricultural. Hooker's is the first printed map of the city and, as such, shows not only what it was like in 1587 but probably what it had been like for the previous three or four hundred years and, to some extent, how it would remain until the end of the 18th century. The south east quarter, East Gate to South Gate, including the Cathedral was inhabited by the well-to-do, with both sides of the High Street and Southgate Street a mixture of shops and merchant's houses. The rest of the city was populated by the poorer artisans and workers, becoming poorer towards and beyond the walls. Yet, as Hooker drew it, the city was full of courts, gardens and even small fields; such industry as there was is mostly confined to the south west slope down to and beyond the West Gate where the whole cloth trade was situated.

But Hooker was to some extent misleading - it was difficult to show that the west end of High Street was narrow and steep, for example. The principal road to the West Gate and thence to the bridge was through the Shambles, Butcher's Row and down Smythen Street; too steep for wheeled traffic, it was only suitable for the pack-horse and the pedestrian brave enough to climb beside the open-drain and it would remain in this state until the 19th century. Hooker shows clearly, however, that there was little development beyond the walls except close to the four main gates and the Water Gate leading down to The Quay.

The maps from the 17th and early 18th centuries are interesting as they all differ slightly in some respects, but all retain the basic layout of the city and its more prominent buildings. Many include the names of such buildings and also the names of churches, and some will include names of areas and large houses outside the city walls. Good examples are the maps in Richard Izacke's history of Exeter and the map included in his son's continuation. The former (7) depicts Exeter in the third quarter of the seventeenth century, while the latter (with Sutton Nicholls plan, 9 illustrated over) presents Exeter in the first quarter of the eighteenth century. However, later maps, such as that of Tozer in 1792, give a much more detailed image of the area within and without the walls (see 15).

During the 17th and 18th centuries, various authors produced their versions of the city's history, and during the early 19th century several more histories were produced, including those of Jenkins (17), Oliver (with an early view of the castle precincts, 35), Freeman (53) and Thomas Brice (1802) etc. Most included a map of the city. Printing processes were being developed year by year, and as books and maps became easier to produce in numbers, so they became more readily available to the public in shops, reading rooms and other similar institutions. As will be seen in the following pages, the mapping of Exeter has been considerable over centuries, and in themselves the maps tell a large part of the city's history.

Andrew Brice, mentioned above, was one of the first people to produce an Exeter newspaper. His first enterprise was *The Postmaster*, subtitled *The Loyal Mercury*. He went on to produce several journals, including *The Weekly Journal*, or the *Old Exeter Journal* as it was also known. After the death of Brice the paper continued being produced by his partner, Barnabas Thorn, and subsequently by Thorn's son until it was purchased by Robert Trewman who renamed it *The Flying Post*.

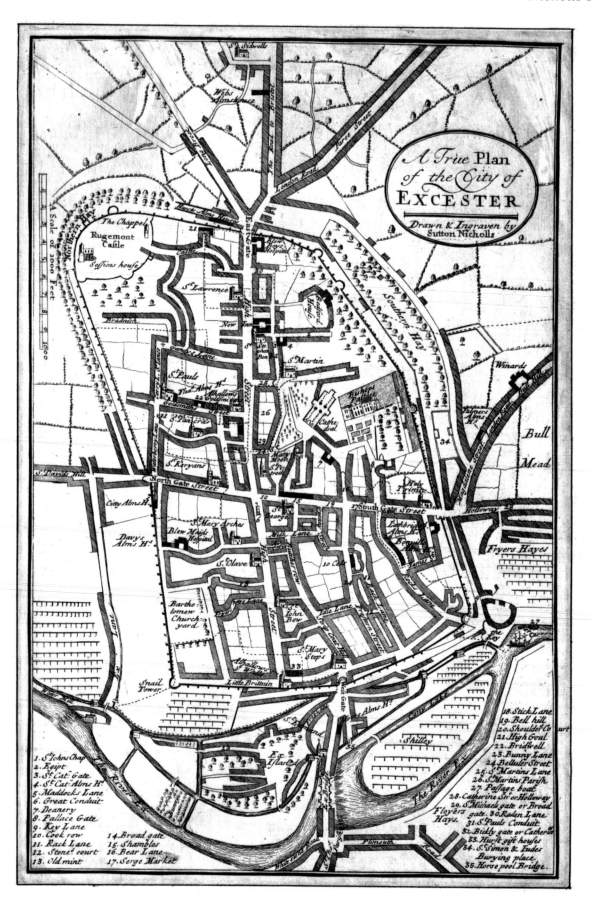

**See Sutton Nicholls entry 9**

## Exeter's national importance

A few centuries ago, Exeter held a proud place in England. It was one of the more important areas for trade, and one of the oldest places in the country. Certainly, in earlier days, Exeter was one of the three most important cities in England. The reasons for this importance are quite simple. Firstly, early Exeter was suitably located on a plateau approximately one hundred feet above the River Exe. The ground around the city was most suitable for excavating building materials - bearing in mind that early buildings in the area were constructed of timber and 'cob', the latter being a mixture of mud, straw and even dung, which, when mixed together and dried out, formed a suitable material to construct walls. The river Exe was easily accessible for a good supply of fresh water, and, in those days, fish in abundance. The area surrounding the city was eminently suitable for agricultural use, the soil being rich and fertile. Hundreds of acres of farmland around Exeter were able to grow large areas of corn and other crops, whilst the fertile meadows allowed cattle and sheep to graze freely. Thus Exeter had a continual supply of fish, meat, and crops, with many grist mills supplying sufficient amounts of flour for making bread. It was, as were most towns and cities of that era, "self sufficient" in most respects.

A famous visitor to remark on Exeter's wealth and success was Daniel Defoe. In the early 1700s he remarked that Exeter was *full of gentry and good company, and yet full of trade and manufacturers also.* Apparently it was said in those days that few places could boast both of these "virtues".

Transport in earlier centuries presented merchants with a problem, for their wares needed to be distributed far and wide, even abroad. Horse traffic was slow, and railways did not come into being until the early nineteenth century, with motorised vehicles arriving much later still. Exeter, however, had the advantage of being close to the English Channel, with a river running alongside the city. Over the years, Exeter developed into a port of great importance, and in those days, boats could sail from the English Channel, up the estuary of the River Exe, and dock alongside the quay in Exeter to load and offload goods. Various buildings still stand adjacent to the quay relating to the work carried out there. A few yards away from the docking area is the Custom House, a magnificent building dating from 1681, and said to be the first commercial building in Exeter constructed of brick. It was from here that all revenues were collected – all goods being weighed on the King's Beam that is still in existence a few yards from the Custom House. Nearby is the Wharfinger's House, where lived the "manager" of the wharf, or quayside. Also nearby is Cricklepit Mill, once a fulling mill but later converted to a corn mill and also used for a time as a saw mill. The mill has, in the past few years, been totally restored and is now in complete working order – a popular tourist attraction.

The undeniable fact of Exeter's prominence in trading by shipping was not appreciated by the Countess Isabella de Fortibus, a member of Devon's Courtenay family. In the 13th century, she decided to construct a weir across the river to prevent large ships going to the port of Exeter. There was, in her mind, solid reasoning in her decision and action.

The Courtenay family were the Earls of Devon, living at Powderham Castle – as indeed they still do. They owned huge tracts of land surrounding the city, including the smaller port of Topsham, a short distance up the estuary from the English Channel. The Countess realised that the family were losing a lot of trade to Exeter, and needed to make more use of the port of Topsham. By preventing shipping heading onwards to Exeter, ships would be forced to offload at Topsham, the nearest port to Exeter, thus providing additional income for the family by way of tolls and fees on the cargoes offloaded at their port. Exeter would be deprived of these fees by the weir being constructed. In 1284 the weir was created, with a small central gap of less than thirty feet, thus allowing only smaller boats to continue up river. The larger sailing ships were now forced to dock at Topsham, paying their dues to the Courtenay family, and then having the added expense of requiring their goods to be transported to Exeter by horse and cart. The area close to that weir is now known as Countess Wear, or sometimes more correctly referred to as Countess Weir, as it perhaps should be known.

The problems surrounding the construction of the weir to prevent Exeter being able to trade by sea were discussed at length by the City Council, and eventually it was decided to create a ship canal to enable shipping to reach Exeter once more. In the mid-1500s work started on the original canal, and that opened in 1566. A few years later work commenced to widen and deepen the canal, to allow larger trading ships to reach Exeter. The canal ran almost parallel to the River, circumnavigating the obtrusive weir and eventually terminating further downstream, just past Topsham. At the city end, the canal terminated at The Basin, where ships could turn and sail out of the city. At long last, goods were again able to reach Exeter's Quay area!

## Exeter's wool and cloth industries

Probably the most important factor that made Exeter a place of considerable wealth and importance was the cloth and woollen trades of the 16th, 17th and 18th centuries. In 1698 Celia Fiennes visited Exeter and gave a glowing report of what she saw and found here.

*"Exeter"*, she wrote, *"... is a town very well built. The streets are well pitched, spacious noble streets, and a vast trade is carried on.....there is an incredible number of serges made and sold in the town. Their market day is Friday which supplies all things like a fair almost. The market for meat, fowl, fish, garden things, and dairy produce takes up three whole streets, besides the large Market House set on stone pillars which runs a great length, on which they lay their packs of serges. Just by is another walk within pillars which is for the yarn. The whole town and country is employed for at least twenty miles around in spinning, weaving, dressing and scouring, fulling and drying of the serges. It turns the most money in a week of anything in England. One week with another there is £10,000 paid in ready money, sometimes £15,000...."*

Fiennes describes Exeter's woollen industry and its various processes – although she stops at describing the actual manufacturing processes involved, probably wisely as these were quite laborious and complicated.

It was at this period that Exeter's woollen and cloth trade started to prosper. Mention has already been made of grist mills, but there were a considerable number of woollen mills in the area as well, located alongside the river. Later there were also paper mills, but the woollen mills were, perhaps, of far more significance in the early days.

A large amount of the combed wool was sent out to the cottage industries of country spinners and weavers who returned it later to market as woven serges. Other towns such as Tiverton carried out the earliest processes but again returning the serge to Exeter. The raw wool was brought in, sorted, spun, combed and woven. The dampened fabrics were then beaten in the fulling-mills, a process in Devon called tucking. The fulled material was then taken to be stretched and dried in the rack fields. When dry it was teased to raise the nap and then sheared for a smooth finish. Finally it went to the drawer to repair blemishes and to the hot pressman. If colour was required this was now done but only to commission. All of this work with the trading and the packing was carried out in the south-west part of the city and down on Exe Island and Shilhay.

Daniel Defoe claimed that Exeter's weekly serge market was second only in size to the Brigg Market at Leeds, in Yorkshire, the largest in England at that time. He further maintained that the Devon woollen industry was the *most important branch of the woollen manufacture in the whole of England*. Exeter was certainly recognised as being of considerable importance within the woollen trade, and also in other trades.

The various mills in the city produced cloth in huge amounts, and this was sold all over the country. Few of these mills are shown on maps. The Fulling Mill at Blackaller Wear is shown on one or two maps and is clearly visible on Tozer's map (15), but others are either not shown or are indiscernible. Later, during the 1600s, serge became more popular as it was far more hard-wearing, and most mills turned to that material to enhance their trade – hence Celia Fiennes' comments noted earlier. Local cloth merchants became extremely wealthy and constructed their out-of-town houses in the suburbs of the city, many of which still exist, although few now remain as private residences, many having been converted into apartments and others used for corporate reasons. One should note the extensive rack-fields - a sign of the extensive fullers' trade. The extent of the industry is shown on various maps by the extent of the rack-fields: two rows in 1587 (1), five fields in 1709 (8), seven fields in 1792 (15), five in 1805 (16) and none by 1845 (31).[1] Rack Lane, close to the West gate, is named after the numerous drying racks located in that street.

Throughout the 18th century Exeter's wool trade slowly decreased due to the considerable number of mills being built in the north of England, and also the impact on trade caused by the European wars. In the middle of the 18th century Exeter's wool trade was only half the size it had been at the beginning of the century. By the end of the 1700s it had virtually died in the city although some woollen and serge racks can still be seen in the

---

[1] After 1688 woollen products were allowed to be exported free of duty and Exeter became a major trading centre for both export and import as well as re-export. Land transport was expensive and difficult and the coastal trade expanded throughout the 18th century, and with the trade both canal and quay grew in importance. The wool trade had two high points: in 1710 the value of the export of serge to Holland was £386,000 (compared to Norwich at £239,000 and London only £20,000); after a period of decline, the serge trade was worth roughly £600,000 in 1777. The collapse that followed was effected first by the American War of Independence and then by the French revolutionary wars. By 1820 the port was only engaged in coastal traffic and by 1820 the woollen trade was almost irrelevant in the city. Vancouver (B&B 70, 1808) placed the collapse much earlier, stating that exports in 1800 were worth only £24,000!

maps of Hayman (16, 17 and 20). It is interesting to note that the only surviving Trade Guild in Exeter is that of the woollen trade – *The Incorporation of Weavers, Fullers and Shearmen*, who still meet at their own Guild hall – Tuckers Hall – in Exeter's Fore Street. This guild hall must not be confused with the magnificent Guildhall in High Street – one of Exeter's oldest buildings still in daily use, mainly for civic functions, although exhibitions and various meetings are frequently held there. The ancient Tuckers Hall, still overseen by a Beadle, is one of Exeter's finest buildings, containing many relics of the trade.

## Exeter toll houses and turnpikes

During the 18th century, roads were being improved largely due to the Turnpike Trusts. Thus travel became easier and quicker, and contact between cities and towns increased, as did trade. Early tracks and roads connecting towns and villages were not 'owned', and were therefore not maintained. With the advent of the Turnpike Trusts, this altered, and roads became an important part of life, not just for businesses, but also for the public. From the fourteenth century, the idea of levying tolls to upkeep roads was in place, but Turnpike roads came into being in the mid seventeenth century. Turnpike Trusts were regulated by Parliament, but the day-to-day running was left to local worthies or councils, who formed a "trust". They were responsible for sections of road, and subsequently charged for the upkeep of them. The system did not reach Devon until the 1750s, and Exeter in 1753. There then began the appearance of turnpikes and toll-gates, with suitable toll-houses alongside. Various charges were set, and tolls were levied according to usage. For example, a person on horseback may be charged one penny, a farmer with a small flock of sheep ten pence, and a carriage with six horses one shilling – but of course ten pence today is vastly different from the 1800s! Exeter had many toll-gates, none of which survive, and only one or two of the former toll houses remain in the area, such as those in Topsham Road and New North Road. The toll system continued until the advent of the railway in England in the early 1800s, but by the end of the 19th century it had virtually ceased. The railway became an easier means of transport for both passengers and goods. Today, of course, the idea of levying tolls is commonplace on roads and bridges in many countries.

Many maps have recorded the existence of Turnpikes and Toll Gates. Some, fortunately, for the historian, name the actual gates - such as the Red Cow Turnpike depicted by Hackett (23) or the toll gate at Parker's Well, clearly seen on later Hayman maps (20). Later it became the custom to write TG (for Toll gate) as Dawson did on his boundary reform maps (24 and 27). Some of the gates were strangely named such as Withybridge on Black Boy Road or Loggerheads at Countess Wear. Sadly, only a few are mentioned on the maps of Exeter. Other maps are extant which show the intended turnpike roads between towns and Thomas Hackett produced a few of these.

## Exeter in the 19th century

So we move on to the nineteenth century, and see an improvement in the city, although the French Wars during the latter part of the 18th century had prevented much of the city's exports going to Europe. Exeter at the beginning of the nineteenth century had around 20,000 citizens. Various areas were literally taken over by the considerable number of wealthy merchants who still survived, despite the Wars. Pennsylvania, for example, was popular for its magnificent views across the city, and several large houses were constructed there, including the splendid properties of Pennsylvania Park. Other areas were to follow the pattern, and out-of-town houses were constructed by the wealthy, with many still surviving to this day. Within the city, large houses were constructed in terraces, such as Colleton Crescent, Barnfield Crescent etc. Other properties were detached, or semi detached, as can be seen in Baring Crescent.

Other areas were to follow the pattern, and out-of-town houses were constructed by the wealthy, with many still surviving to this day. A good example can be found in the houses of Topsham Road. *Larkbeare,* seen in Braun & Hogenberg (1618) and Izacke (1677), was one of three properties known with this name. *Great Larkbeare* and *Little Larkbeare* stood at the bottom of Holloway Street, at the junction of today's Robert's Road. The modern *Larkbeare* still stands next to St Leonard's church. *Mount Radford,* was earlier known as *Radford Place* (see Speed, 1610). In the 1700s, this house was occupied by the Baring family, creators of Barings Bank. Adjacent to *Mount Radford* was *Parkerswell,* seen in Hayman (1805). This house was probably constructed a few years before, possibly at the end of the 18th century. *Coaver* was probably also built at the end of the 18th century, or the early 19th century and is shown in Hayman's maps of 1806 and 1828. *Bellair,* also seen in Hayman (1806 and 1828), was built in 1710 by wealthy grocer John Vowler. Both *Coaver* and *Bellair,* together with their respective land, have in recent years been incorporated into Devon County Hall, headquarters of the Devon County Council. Maps before 1900 do not extend much further than *Bellair,* but there are several other properties in Topsham Road that were built by wealthy merchants, and these include *Otago, Buckerell Lodge, Wear House, Fairfield, Abbeville, Feltrim* etc.

Several local businessmen became rich as a result of the "building boom" of the time, including brickworks owner and property developer John Sampson, and builders William Hooper and Matthew Nosworthy. Much of their work can still be seen in Heavitree, Polsloe, Southernhay and other areas. Hooper, for example, was responsible for Higher Summerlands (destroyed in the Exeter Blitz), Lower Summerlands, Baring Place, the elegant Chichester Place, and much of St. Leonard's Road. Nosworthy is remembered for his properties in Barnfield Crescent, Colleton Crescent and the original Dix's Field (also destroyed in the Exeter Blitz). Sampson's Lane, in Polsloe, is named after John Sampson. Two of Exeter's markets, the Higher Market in Queen Street, and the Lower Market in Fore Street were built by Hooper, but designed by the respected architect Charles Fowler, who was also responsible for the design of London's Covent Garden, and, more locally, the gatehouse of Powderham Castle, home of the Earls of Devon. The Higher Market still exists, but in its new role as a shopping mall.

Markets were of considerable importance to the city, being held on Mondays, Wednesdays and Fridays, although later reduced to just Fridays. Fairs would be held on the third Wednesday of February, May and July, and the second Wednesday in December. The markets and fairs were for both for cattle and merchandise. The ancient Fair named *Crollditch* is now *The Lammas Fair* and is still acknowledged in the city.

## Transport improves

Victorian Exeter saw the arrival of the railway. Despite Besley including the line of the South Devon Railway in his maps of 1836 and 1839 (20) and projecting a line to cross Bonhay and Great Shilhay, the first trains did not arrive in Exeter until 1844, the line being officially opened on 1st May with a grand dinner being held in the goods shed. And, of course, the Bristol and Exeter Railway Station was built near the Red Cow Inn and the line crossed the river avoiding Bonhay etc. as seen in Warren's map, also executed for Besley (30). Within 20 years Queen Street station was constructed as the rival London & South Western Railway entered the city. Its arrival was forecast on Featherstone's small map circa 1858 (40). The railway system throughout the country was fast increasing as business people saw a much quicker and easier method of transporting their wares from one place to another, and passengers were able to reach their destinations far more quickly. A journey from London, for which with the *Telegraph* post coach had taken 17 hours, could now be done in just four and a half on the express train. And despite low wages, the average worker was able to afford a ride on the railway on the increasing number of free days.

Wages were comparatively low and hours were often long, with some workers toiling from 6.00 am until 5.30 pm. In the mid 1800s, a labourer would be earning less than one pound a week, but more skilled people were able to command from four pence to six pence an hour, and for a fifty-six hour week they were able to earn almost two pounds. By the early 1900s, working hours reduced to around 48 per week and there were more public holidays but pay rates remained fairly constant.

At the same time, the Exeter Canal was seeing a boom in trade, with ships bringing coal, timber, oil and other goods into the city. On the Quayside, large warehouses were constructed (still standing and well-used today) by businesses who relied on shipping for bringing their goods to Exeter. Large iron foundries were constructed in the lower part of the city, the Victorian era being renowned for ornate ironwork in buildings and in the streets of the city. Three of Exeter's best-known foundries were Bodleys (founded 1790), Willeys (founded 1860) and Garton & King, the latter being able to boast of their beginnings in the mid 1600s!

The tramcar system of public transport in Exeter started with horse drawn vehicles, but at the end of the 19th, electric trams were in operation – powered by electricity running from the Rockfield Works in New North Road. This is shown as *"Electricity Station"* in Walker Boutall (1895) and Ward Lock (1898). In 1905 a new Power Station was opened in Haven Road, and the Rockfield Works was sold. From 1905 until 1931 trams continued to be powered from Haven Road.

To provide for this increase in transport needs, new roads had to be built and some maps are still available which show the thoughts of those contemporary city planners. Hackett's maps, especially, indicate the road needs of the 1830s and project the routes of the New North Devon Road past the barracks and the New Road extending from Bedford Crescent out into the suburbs (see 21, 22 and *Hackett II* opposite).

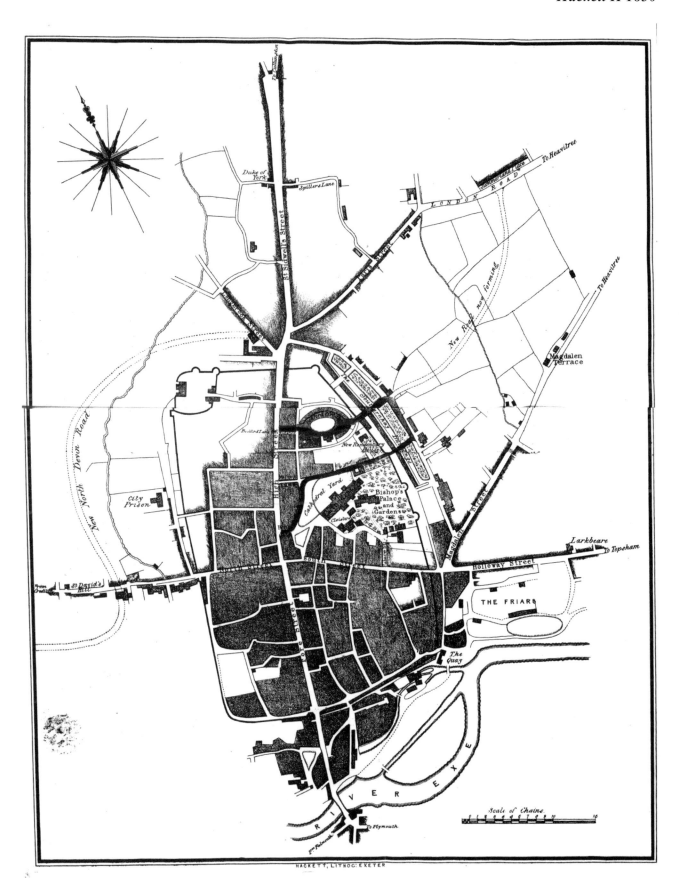

**See Hackett II entry 23**

## Exeter as a Meeting Place

Being such an important city, Exeter was obviously the place for merchants, traders, and the general public to meet. The ale-houses mentioned previously were, of course gathering places for all and sundry. It is claimed that Sir Francis Drake took coffee in Mol's Coffee House, and ale in the Ship Inn in Martin's Lane. The former claim is debatable. John Dyer leased the building (previously the Anneuller's College) from 1585 and some Armada negotiations took place there but it wasn't really a coffee house until about 1726 when it was advertised in Brice's *Weekly Journal.* A large room on the first floor is decorated with no less than forty-six coats of arms of the more noted Devon families who presumably made Mol's a rendezvous when they visited Exeter. However, hotels and larger ale houses were frequently used for meetings. Some two hundred members of the Devonshire Chamber of Agriculture met at the Half Moon Hotel, in High Street four times a year. In 1850 they played host to the Royal Agricultural Show and two guides were produced specially for the occasion (see 33 and 34).

The Exeter Literary Society, established in 1841, met at their premises in Barnfield Road, now The Barnfield Theatre. Here there were reading rooms in which the weekly lectures took place, with smaller discussion groups using other rooms in the building. In 1850 the Society had no less than 550 members. Maps will show earlier meeting places such as Taylors Hall and James Meeting Place.

There were other meeting places of perhaps more formal surroundings. The Devon and Exeter Institution, at No 7 The Close, is a reading room and library for its members. The Institution was founded in 1813 *"for promoting Science Literature and Art, and for illustrating the Natural and civil History of the County of Devon and the city of Exeter"* and remains in constant use today for meetings, lectures and research.

The Victoria Hall in Queen Street, no longer in existence, was built in 1869 to provide a room large enough to accommodate two thousand people expected for the British Association Meeting held in Exeter that year. There were also ancillary lecture rooms, committee rooms and a sale room. It was also the venue for concerts, exhibitions, public dinners and balls. During the Meeting it was used as the location for the Geography section as well as for Inaugural and Other Addresses (illustrated below).

In 1894 Exeter was again host to a prestigious meeting when the Church Congress was held in October (61).

### *British Association 1869*

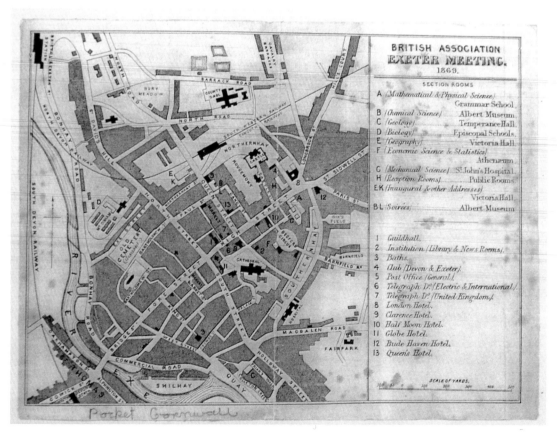

**See British Association entry 43**

## Changes in the City

Exeter's layout has, of course, changed dramatically since Roman days, although the basic "enclosed" city can still be seen in aerial photographs, and much of the Roman wall is still in place. Probably one of the most important changes was that of the High Street/Fore Street link to the west. Hooker's map of 1587 shows the High Street continuing down to the River Exe, but to the northern side of the West Gate. The road that ran down directly to the West Gate was Stepcote Hill – then the main exit route from the city centre. Nicholls has Strip Coat Hill! Going out of the West Gate took the traveller across the bridge crossing the Exe, and into St Thomas. Stepcote Hill today remains very much as it was, but it must have been very difficult to traverse as it is steep and cobbled - although William of Orange managed it (with 200 blacks from his plantations) in 1688. The upper storeys of houses corbelled out and the first floors on either side were extremely close. The layout is clearly shown in Braun & Hogenberg's map of 1618, and in Donn's map of 1765. However, by the late eighteenth century things had changed, and Tozer's map of 1872 shows the High Street leading down to Fore street, which in turn went down to the new river crossing to the north of the West Gate. Stepcote Hill was now redundant as a main exit.

Exe Bridge was at one time a mere timber structure, replaced in the 1200s by a new stone structure of seventeen arches, as can be seen in various maps of the 16th and 17th centuries. In the latter part of the 18th century, this bridge was also replaced, although several of the original arches can now been seen between the plain and uninteresting 20th century structures, Exe Bridge North and Exe Bridge South.

Rocque's map of 1764 shows a Workhouse situated a considerable distance from the City, on the London Road. This was recently the site of the Royal Devon and Exeter Hospital at Heavitree, although much of that (at the time of writing) is set to be demolished for a supermarket! Tozer is interesting as he shows several important changes. We now see the new Devon County Gaol, together with smaller changes such as New Cut, which takes the pedestrian from Southernhay to the Cathedral. Also depicted is the Theatre in Waterbeer Street, but although this building was in being in the early 1700s, it is not shown as such prior to Rocque. The building can be seen, though not named as a Theatre. In 1787 a new Theatre was constructed at the junction of Southernhay and the new Bedford Circus, and can be seen on Tozer's map. This theatre was destroyed by fire in 1820, and was replaced by another in 1821. In 1885 that building was also destroyed by fire, but never replaced. For some reason, Freeman's map of 1887 and Cassell's of 1888 both continue to show the theatre.

Perhaps Bedford Circus deserves a special mention. No longer existing, thanks to the bombing raids in 1942, Bedford Circus has a "special" place in Exeter's recent history. Originally the site of a Dominican Monastery, it later became Bedford House, the family home of Lord John Russell, the Duke of Bedford. It was in this house that Queen Henrietta Maria (wife of Charles I) gave birth to Princess Henrietta, having stopped off at Exeter during the Civil War in England, as she fled this country for homeland, France. The house was demolished in 1783, to allow Bedford Circus to be constructed. Portman (1966) states that the Circus was completed in 1825. It contained some of Exeter's finest Georgian houses, most of which were five storeys if their basements are included. The properties were largely owned, or at least occupied, by professional businessmen such as accountants, solicitors, architects etc. It was severely damaged during 1942, and although one or two properties such as Bedford Chapel could have been saved, the whole area was demolished and the new Bedford Street laid out. Sadly the modern construction was nowhere near as attractive as the original. Bedford Circus can be seen in various maps including Hackett (23), where the Bedford Chapel is shown as a detached building to the south of the Circus – although not named as such. Brown/Schmollinger 1835 and later maps do name it.

A myriad of changes took place during the late 1700s, and early 1800s, but far too many to individually mention here. Major developments included the extension to the port. In Hayman's map of 1828 we see the "proposed Basin" – an important feature of Exeter to this day – for it stands at the end of the Exeter Ship Canal, the only way that ships can now reach the City (see above). One of the next important changes was the introduction of a new road from the High Street towards the new projected railway station at St David's. This road was built in 1834, and was named Higher Market Street until some years later, when it was re-named Queen Street to honour the then monarch, Queen Victoria. The first map to show this street appears to be that of Brown and Schmollinger in 1835. It is interesting to note that on this same map, the gates of the City are no longer shown, as the last gate to be demolished was the North Gate, in 1834.

The name Besley is probably more associated with Street Directories, but of course many of the directories included maps. The first map of Exeter specifically commissioned for Besley (by Warren in 1845) is interesting in that it depicts the new railway system running along the west side of the city. By this time, considerable areas of land outside the city walls had now been developed for housing. This map when compared with maps of the 1700s, for example, shows how this development evolved. Warren's map also clearly shows the two Markets, Higher (Queen Street) and Lower (Market Street), both constructed in the 1830s to the design of Charles Fowler.

Oliver's reproduction of Norden's plan of the Castle, which later became a court house, is of particular interest today because from 2004 the castle ceased to be used for Court and civic purposes, and became the property of a developer who planned great things – including a restaurant and apartments that, in 2010, have only partially come to fruition. Early maps (e.g. Tozer) depict the small Chapel of St Mary that once stood just inside the Norman gatehouse, but the chapel was demolished in the late 18th century. It was later replaced with the Castle Keeper's cottage, which is shown on later maps, but can be confused with the original chapel.

From 1850 it is impossible to list the changes that have taken place in the City, but many of these changes can be seen on the maps of the late 1800s and early 1900s when one looks carefully. This was the period when many roads, streets and crescents were created in the city. Since then the City has seen constant change, with huge areas of housing and general development.

The most significant changes to the City in modern times took place during the 1941/1942 bombing raids on Exeter during the Second World War.

## Exeter in the 1939-45 War

Although the events of the 1939-1945 war are outside the scope of this present volume and have been discussed in full in other publications it is, perhaps, important to mention how it changed the face of Exeter. In 1942 Exeter received a series of bombing raids by the German Luftwaffe. Exeter was of little importance to the Germans and was probably simply unlucky to become a target. Air Marshal Sir Arthur Harris, then in charge of Bomber Command, had wanted to experiment on bringing in waves of aircraft instead of a single squadron and ordered experimental raids to be carried out on Lübeck, a small, attractive town on the Baltic shores of Germany. Lübeck was of little significance, apart from its location close to a German submarine base. The raids on Lübeck left the town a smouldering ruin, causing Hitler to order attacks on English towns and cities that were, like Lübeck, historic and of great beauty. However, Exeter did have a fighter station responsible for the airspace west of Portland. It is popular belief that targets were chosen from the *Baedeker Guide Books*, the German equivalents of the Murray or A & C Black guides of Great Britain.

During the raids on Exeter - which became known as *Baedaker* or *reprisal* raids - much of the city's historic centre was devastated, with many fine buildings lost. Especially hard hit was the area where the High Street and Bedford Street join and some of the buildings to be destroyed included Deller's Café at the corner, a splendid building on three storeys and not just a café, but an important meeting place for all and sundry. Other buildings destroyed included the delightful Bampfylde House, which although internally ravaged by fire, was capable of being restored but was demolished, and the Hall of the Vicars Choral, the home for several vicars attached to the Cathedral. The gas works at Haven Bank, shown on many pre-1900 maps, was bombed but suffered the loss of only one tank but the Lower Market was caught in the blazes around South Street, Market Street, Coombe Street and Fore Street and was lost. The city library in Castle Street was taken over as a control centre, but was largely destroyed by fire and had to be evacuated. The lovely Bedford Circus, its development plotted so carefully in the 19th century maps, was destroyed and demolished. The Lower Market was largely destroyed in the Exeter Blitz, but the granite shell remained and could have been restored, but was, sadly, demolished.

Since WWII Exeter has become a much larger city, if not as beautiful as it was. In more recent years, Exeter has taken in outlying suburbs, such as Alphington and, Pinhoe and now has some 125,000 residents, and is a thriving, bustling community. Yet it has changed dramatically, possibly for the worse in many respects. In his book W.G. Hoskins (1960) regretted that Exeter was no longer a city of culture. There was, he said, a profound difference between modern Exeter and that of one hundred years ago. That, of course, is due to progress and modernisation, but Hoskins is right in saying that the culture of Exeter – and probably many similar cities – has changed. So has the architecture, so has the size and layout. Indeed, so has the population itself changed, for we all now live in a modern society that reflects little on the life of centuries past. Was Exeter a better place in medieval times, or was The Georgian era better? Did the Victorians live a better, more cultured life, or are we now living in better times? Perhaps it is better for the reader to decide.

Despite all the change, despite the intrusion of past invaders, despite the devastation caused by the last War, and despite modern challenges, Exeter is still a delightful place in which to live and work.[1]

---

[1] I would like to acknowledge the help of both Andrew Passmore B.Sc. and David Cornforth.

# THE PRINTED MAPS

## of

# EXETER

# 1587 - 1901

# 300 Years of Exeter History

# *The Catalogue*

## 1.   John Hooker                                                          *1587*

The first printed maps of the city appeared towards the end of the 16th century. Exeter was in the extremely fortunate situation of having an antiquarian and historian as its first Chamberlain and one who was also both surveyor and draftsman. John Hooker (*c*1527-1601) was the son of Robert Hooker or Robert Vowell, Mayor of Exeter in 1529. The Vowell family, prominent Exeter citizens for a number of generations, obtained the name Hooker in the 15th century but used the name Vowell regularly. John's parents died when he was ten and he was brought up by Doctor Moreman, vicar of Menhinit in Cornwall. He went to Oxford to study civil law, and then travelled and studied under leading protestant figures in Germany, France, Italy and Spain. He returned to France but, because of the wars there, returned to Exeter where he subsequently married and pursued his interests in history and antiquities. In 1549 he was in Exeter at the time of the siege during the Prayer Book Rebellion and in 1555 the magistrates of the city elected him to be their first Chamberlain. He was engaged by Sir Peter Carew as legal advisor over property disputes in Ireland and Hooker became a member of both the English and the Irish parliaments.

In the following years he commissioned a number of his own works from London publishers which were often intended as New Year gifts. He wrote many histories among which was a *Catalogue of the Bishops of Exeter and an Historical Record of the Province of Devon* and finally his *Antique Description and Account of the City of Exeter*, which was not printed until 1765 by Andrew Price of Exeter. As an influential member of the Exeter society it is highly likely that John Hooker would have met Christopher Saxton when he was surveying Devon for his county map published in 1575 (B&B 1), and it is probably no coincidence that the Flemish engraver Remigius Hogenberg engraved both the county and the city maps. This map was commissioned in London by Hooker, possibly inspired by Hogenberg's 1559 map of London.

Title: **Isca Damnoniorum: britanice Kaier penhuelgorte: Saxonice Monketon: Latine Exonia: Anglice Excancestre vel Excestre at nunc vulgo Exeter: Urbs peratiqua, et Emporium celeberrimum.**
Size: 350 x 525 mm. There is a scale bar but no scale is entered.
Signature: *Opera et impensis Joannis Hokeri generosi ac huius Civitatis quaestoris, hanc tabella sculpsit Remigius Hogenbergius Anno Dei 1587.*

The plan is a bird's eye view, looking north-east, with the river flowing left to right. This view, much copied by the early map-makers, brings with it considerable fore-shortening and to a plan much inaccuracy. The names of the principal streets, churches and buildings are given with boats and fishermen on the river and a crane (marked Crane Seller) on the *Key*. Racks for drying the wool can be seen to the southwest of the city at Snail's Tower with just a single line at Shilhay.
The title is in a plain rectangle at the top with the Royal Arms and the City Arms (granted in 1567). Just above the empty scale bar is a pair of dividers and, in the left corner, Hooker's own arms and his motto *Post Mortem Vita*. As described here only a single copy is known, bought by the British Library in 1897 for 16 guineas, but there are a number of later states extant (see Appendix A). In the third state (illustrated) the road from Larkbeare to St. Leonard's and Radford Place takes a distinctive right bend.
Further manuscript maps drawn by Hooker were printed and published in the late nineteenth century (see 59 and 60).

**1.**                                                                                    *John Hooker 1587*

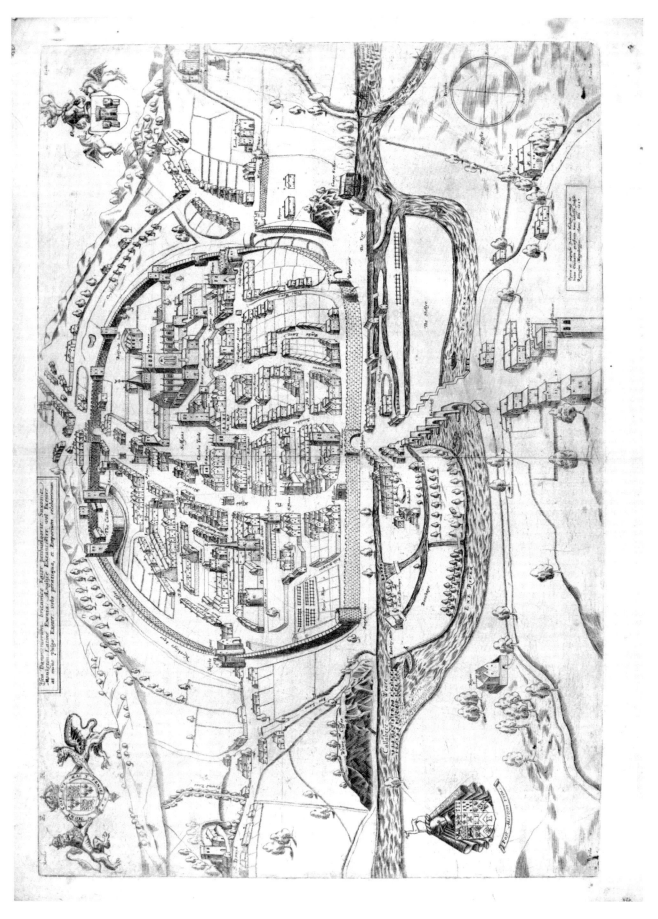

## 2.   *John Speed*                                                                                      *1610*

John Hooker's map was among the first printed maps of any of the cities and towns of England, and his city plan became the example and the only original printed plan of the city for almost 150 years. Like so much of the cartographers' art Hooker's plan was copied frequently, either in the early 17th century as the authentic map of the city or later as a descriptive map of its time.

The most influential of the copyists chose either of two forms: most used a small scale reduction, with or without the lettered references - John Speed in 1610-11 included this in his map of the county (B&B 6); or like Braun and Hogenberg they copied the plan at nearly the original scale and repeated the same lettering. Speed's own copy of Hooker was copied until 1749 and Hogenberg reproductions until 1895. The subsequent 'copies' repeat the city plan with varying amounts of the surrounding country and decorations.

John Speed (1552-1629) was born in Cheshire and like his father became a tailor. By 1580 he had moved to London and had become a freeman of the Merchant Tailors Company. But he had also become a keen amateur historian and joined the Society of Antiquarians, where he would have met William Camden, a famous historian, and Christopher Saxton, responsible for the first printed county maps of English shires, among others. He became interested in maps and by 1598 he was producing his own maps for the Company. Fulke Greville, M.P., Chancellor of the Exchequer and friend of Queen Elizabeth I, arranged for Speed to have an allowance to write a history of England and arranged for him to use a room in the London Custom House. As an historian he was a great gatherer of information. His maps were based on Saxton's and those of John Norden, but he travelled extensively and his maps contained much local information including the lines of the hundreds and, for Devon, the inset map of Exeter based on Hooker.

Speed prepared his county maps over a period of some years[1] and in 1610-11 his *Theatre of the Empire of Great Britain* was published. In 1627 he completed his atlas *A Prospect of the Most Famous Parts of the World* and this was then commonly bound combined with the *Theatre* and together they became the first World Atlas produced by an Englishman. The county map was reissued many times until approx. 1770, both in the atlas and as separate sheets.

Title: ***EXCESTER*** on the county map ***DEVONSHIRE WITH EXCESTER DESCRIBED***.
Size: The inset is small, measuring only 132 x 155 mm, and has no scale (circa 1 Mile = 30 mm). The City Arms are top right within the inset with the title top left.
Signatures (on county map only): *Performed by Ihon Speede And are to be sold in popes-head Alleye by Iohn Sudburi & George humble. Cum privilegio.*

The plan is a reduced copy of Hooker's plan of 1587, covering the same area and again with North to the left. The only writing within the walls are the numbers referring to the list above the plan, however numbers 49 (the Water–gate) and 50 (the Quay) are missing from the list. The Castle's western barbican is pronounced and the river, flowing down Combe Street with the outfall through the wall, is clearly shown. Outside the city Radford Place, St. Leonard and Larkbeare can be seen.
 Due probably to damage to the printing plate, in 1689 Philip Lea commissioned Francis Lamb to copy Christopher Saxton's map of Devon but including a number of changes such as inclusion of John Speed's inset plan of Exeter (B&B 19) [2]. Although the county map was redrawn, and as such was a newly engraved map, the actual inset plan was a direct copy with the same reference numbers and has not been included as a new map. Although the county map's signature changed as the plates changed hands the only change to the Exeter inset occurred in 1743 when some details were strengthened and the stonework to the walls became almost obliterated by angled shading. Illustrated is the Exeter plan from the Bassett and Chiswell county map, c.1676.

---

[1] A single proof of the Devon map is known for 1608 and the first edition of the *Theatre* was published 1610/1611.

[2] Lea acquired most of the Saxton plates but two were obviously missing, as Devon and Northumberland were re-engraved. The most obvious differences to the Saxton map are the inclusions of the shields of arms of notable families (left) and the inset plan of Exeter (bottom right) as included by Speed.

**2.**

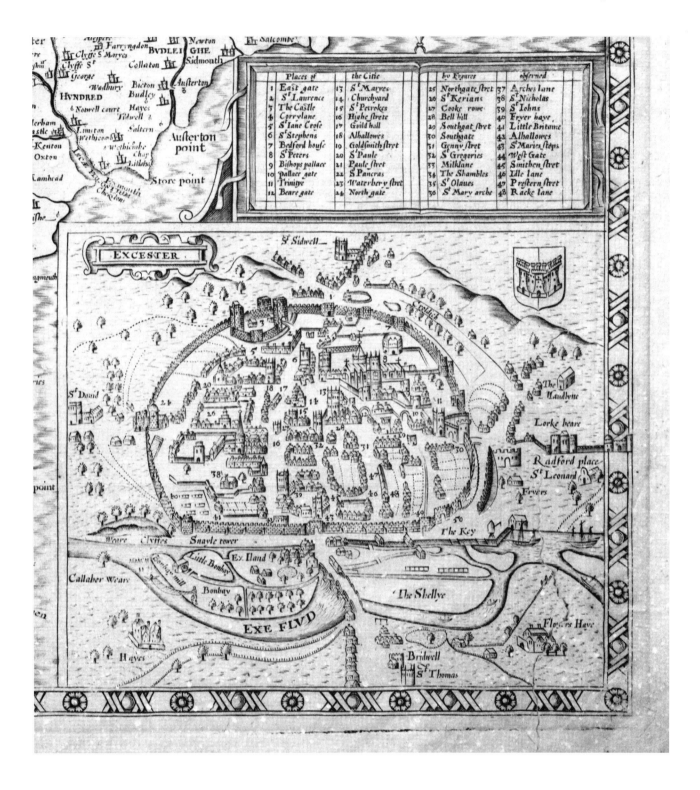

| | Places of | | the Citie | | by Figures | | observed |
|---|---|---|---|---|---|---|---|
| 1 | East gate | 13 | S˙t Maryes | 25 | Northgate stret | 37 | Arches lane |
| 2 | S˙t Laurence | 14 | Churchyard | 26 | S˙t Kerians | 38 | S˙t Nicholas |
| 3 | The Castle | 15 | S˙t Petrokes | 27 | Cooke rowe | 39 | S˙t Iohns |
| 4 | Corrylane | 16 | Highe strete | 28 | Bell hill | 40 | Fryer haye |
| 5 | S˙t Iane Crose | 17 | Guild hall | 29 | Southgat stret | 41 | Little Britane |
| 6 | S˙t Stephens | 18 | Alhallowes | 30 | Southgate | 42 | Alhallowes |
| 7 | Bedford house | 19 | Goldsmith stret | 31 | Genny stret | 43 | S˙t Maries steps |
| 8 | S˙t Peters | 20 | S˙t Paule | 32 | S˙t Gregories | 44 | West Gate |
| 9 | Bishops pallace | 21 | Paule stret | 33 | Milklane | 45 | Smithen stret |
| 10 | pallace gate | 22 | S˙t Pancras | 34 | The Shambles | 46 | Idle lane |
| 11 | Trinitye | 23 | Waterbery stret | 35 | S˙t Olaues | 47 | Prestern stret |
| 12 | Beare gate | 24 | North gate | 36 | S˙t Mary arche | 48 | Racke lane |

## 3.    *Braun & Hogenberg*                                                           *1618*

The German partnership of Georg Braun and Frans Hogenberg copied Hooker at a similar scale thus laying the path for the larger series of Hooker-based plans. Georg Braun (1541-1622) was born in Cologne. Frans (or Francis) Hogenberg (c.1536-1588), and his brother, Remigius (Remy, 1536-1587) were also of German descent but had fled from the Dutch town of Mechelen to England during a period of religious unrest. Frans returned to the Netherlands but Remigius remained in England. Braun and Hogenberg, together with engravers such as Georg Hoefnagel, Daniel Freese and Heinrich Rantzau compiled a city atlas. Their *Civitates Orbis Terrarum* was intended as a companion work to the *Theatrum Orbis Terrarum* (of Abraham Ortelius), or atlas of the world and was edited by Georg Braun. Six volumes were issued between 1572 and 1618 and it was in the final volume that Exeter was included: *Theatri Praecipuarum Totius Urbium Liber Sextus. Anno MIXVIII... Georgius Braun et Franciscus Hogenbergius.*[1] Remigius Hogenberg had engraved Hooker's original plan in 1587, and it is probably through him the plan came to Frans.

Title: **CIVITAS EXONIAE (vulgo Excester) URBIS PRIMARIA IN COMITATU DEVONIAE**.
Size: 317 x 395 mm but with no scale and no signature.

This is a Hooker's 1587 plan though slightly smaller but exquisitely engraved. The title is on a banner and the plan has three coats of arms: The Royal Arms supported by a lion and a dragon; the City's Arms, supported by pegassi; and Hooker's own arms with a note *Insignia Iohannis Hooker* (bottom left). This again is a bird's eye view with the country to the east, stopping like Hooker, on the line of hills. The most noticeable difference is the reduced area. In the foreground the tower of St. Thomas is brought nearer to the river and the adjacent houses are crowded together. On the left hand side Pound Lane is cut off and St. David's is moved to Exe Lane. Yet the shadowed building faces are changed, the west barbican is almost lost as is the stream down Combe Street, without its out-fall through the walls. Most churches are named, as are some streets and while the boats repeat there are now pedestrians (see detail opposite; note also the Great Conduit). Larkbeare and Radford Place are now in a line, the crane seller is still active and the Bridwell of Speed becomes the Brydewol.

Some copies have plain backs but most have Latin, French or German texts initially on the left side of the reverse, on both sides for later reissues, but there were no changes to the plan. There were a number of copies including Daniel Lysons 1822 (B&B 89) and Edward Freeman 1887 (c.f.).

Exeter was a crowded and socially divided city. As early as 1525[2], the wealthier merchants lived in the four parishes of St. Petrock and St. Mary Arches, St. Olave and St. Stephen, in effect in the centre of the city or close to the Cathedral. Within the walls, the poorest lived in the parishes of St. John, All Hallows on the Walls and St. Mary Steps, in effect the Old Britayne quarter of Saxon days (or *Little Britaine* on Speed). This division was also reflected in the houses. The well-to-do merchant's house still contained the shop and the warehouse with a court and garden. The hall was the eating chamber with the parlour as the family room. Above there were up to five bedrooms, with possibly servants' rooms above. Below or next to the hall was the kitchen and buttery and below them a cellar.[3] Whereas a weaver's house, socially divided for example, contained merely the hall, two bedrooms, a kitchen and the shop. When one went further down and out into Duryard or St. Sidwell's one room would have to suffice. This was still the medieval pattern, and explains the crowded plans of Hooker in 1600. This layout would remain so on Ichabod Fairlove's plan of 1709 (entry 8) and even into the 19th century.

---

[1] The preface was signed by Antonius Hierat & Abrahamus Hogenberg. The text was by Abraham Ortel (i.e. Ortelius) & Cornelius Caymox.

[2] See, for example, Hoskins (1960) *2000 Years in Exeter* and MacCaffrey (1958) *Exeter 1540-1640*.

[3] A good example is the 1603 inventory of the late Mayor, Richard Bevys cloth merchant, where his house is described as such. It was drawn up in some fifty accounts and in summary valued his estate as £3284.9s.2d-. DA/XLI/1909.

**3.**                                                      ***Braun & Hogenberg 1618***

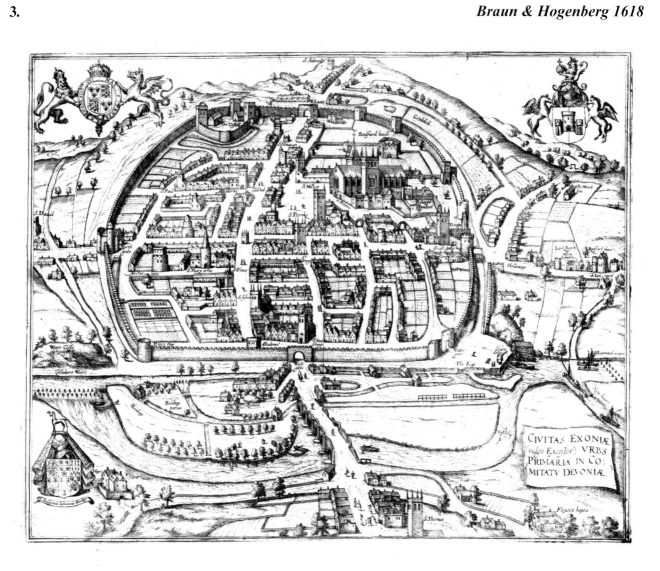

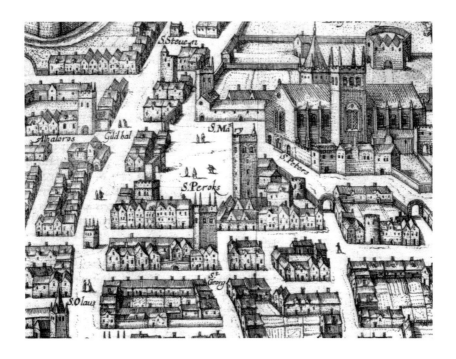

Between 1637 and 1677 four different copies of Speed appeared, three in works published on the European market and one by a local historian.

### 4.  *Daniel Meisner*                                                                                                    *1637*

Daniel Meisner[1], an author and poet, was born in Komothau, Bohemia. He planned the publication of a collection of city plans but died in 1625 before *Thesaurus Philo-Politicus, Das ist Politisches Schatzkästlein guter Herren und bestendiger Freund*, was finished (published 1623 to 1637). The many views illustrated in the work usually include allegorical images and moralizing captions in Latin and German. Once complete, Meisner's *Sciagraphia Cosmica* was published in Nuremberg in 1637 and reissued the following year. The early editions were published by Paulus Fürst in two volumes. This magnificent work included 800 finely engraved views of cities, forts and castles from all over the world.

Title:   **EXCESTER in Engellandt**
Size: 95 x 140 mm but no scale or signature.

This version is unique in that it has text panels above and below: *Immoderatus Amor Interitum Causat* (Excessive love causes death) (top), and *Inter Serpentes mirabilis arte cupido est, Faemina namys suum perdit amore virum* as well as the German translation (bottom): Between serpents desire is wonderful, for the female destroys its mate by love. There is a printer´s mark **16** which was changed to **G46** in the second and subsequent reissues (5 to 1704). There is a letter **H** bottom left.[2]
The map is a very crude copy of Speed, with less detail, little similarity in the street pattern, there are no references and below the river serpent eats serpent. The title is in a small strip and the city coat of arms is badly distorted.

### 5.  *Matthäus Merian*                                                                                                 *1650*

Matthäus Merian (b. 1593 in Basel) served an apprenticeship as copperplate engraver under Friedrich Meyer after leaving grammar school. After spending time in Strasburg, Nancy and Paris he returned to Basel where he produced some of his first town plans (circa 1610-1615). He travelled again before he moved to Frankfurt to work for Johann Theodor de Bry, a well-respected publisher. Together with his son of the same name and Martin Zeiler he worked on a multi-volume work of town views and maps of German-speaking areas, *Topographia Germaniae*. Started in 1642 the work consisted of 16 volumes by 1654 and by 1688 the 30 volumes now included illustrations of other European areas such as France, Italy and Crete. This was one of the most ambitious of all publishing ventures of the time and was issued in many editions. Exeter was one of 17 towns of Great Britain and Ireland which appeared in the year that Merian died (1650) and also in J. C. Beer's *Das neu-beharnischte Grosz-Britannien* published in Nuremberg in 1690.

Title: **Exonia Excester**
Size: 160 x 130 mm with no scale or signatures.

This is a near copy of Speed's inset but without the reference table or numbers, people or ships, extended east and west with the title on an ornate banner below the City's Arms in a leaf cartouche. There are minor irregularities to buildings and trees outside of the city walls.

---

[1] Both Meisner and Meissner are found in biographies. The complete work went under the title *Sciagraphia Cosmica, Oder: eigentliche Abbildung, Achthundert der mehrentheils vornehmsten Städte, Vestungen und Schlösser, so allenthalben in allen Theilen der Welt berümt sind.*
[2] It has been suggested that the letter **H** stands for Hermannides. This is unlikely as the plan by Hermannides (1661, see over) is similar to Merian (1650) and not Meisner.

**4.**
*Daniel Meisner 1637*

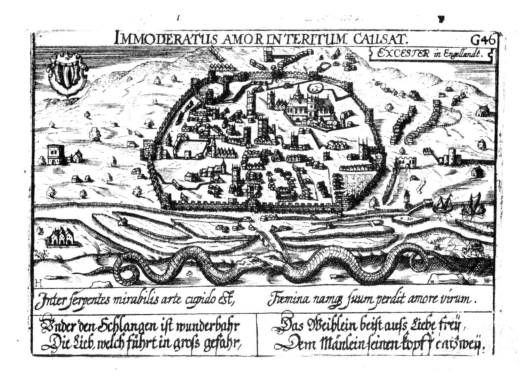

**5.**
*Matthäus Merian 1650*

## 6.    *Rutgerus Hermannides*                                                                  *1661*

The first work which was solely devoted to British towns appeared in 1661 and contained a general map, a map of London and 30 town plans including that of Exeter. The map was by Rutgerus Hermannides, Professor of History at Harderwijk, and the volume was *Britannia Magna* published in Amsterdam in that year.

Title:  **EXONIA EXCESTER**
Size: 105 x 130 mm with no scale or signatures.

This map has the City Arms (top left). It is a near copy of Speed's inset, or more correctly of Merian, but without the reference table or numbers, people or ships; the only lettering apart from the title is *Exe Fluvius.*
The plate was subsequently printed and published in Pierre (Peter) van der Aa's *La galérie Agreeable du monde* in 1729. The plate was modified with the addition of a decorative top border which includes a key to 7 sites (and other places are named on the map) and then placed within a trompe l'oeil engraved frame which doubled the dimensions of the print but retaining title as before. Additions include the signature: *A. Leide, Chez Pierre Vander Aa, Marhand, Libraire* (below the map detail). This work also included a map of the county of Devon (B&B 13.4) by Pieter van den Keere.

## 7.    *Richard Izacke*                                                                          *1677*

Richard Izacke was appointed Chamberlain of Exeter in 1653, like Hooker before him. His main work, *Antiquities Of The City Of Exeter* with a history of Exeter and a list of its most important official representatives was *Collected by Richard Izacke, Esquire Chamberlain thereof* and published in London by Richard Marriott with the *Imprimatur* of *G Jane* and dated *October 20, 1676*, although it wasn't issued until 1677. Both this first edition[1], and the second edition[2] which appeared in 1681, contained a map of Exeter copied fairly closely from Speed's (inset) map of 1610. Although very similar to Speed's, with the same references (1 to 50 on map; only 1 to 48 in table *Figures of Reference*), it is somewhat wider and shows further buildings both east and west. As on Speed's map item 32, St. Georges Church, is incorrectly labelled as St. Gregories.
Who drew and engraved the map is not known. The work was reissued in an extended and revised version, by the then Chamberlain, Samuel Izacke, in 1724, complete with a new map (see Sutton Nicholls).

Title: **A MAPP OF the CITY of EXETER**
Size: 160 x 193 mm with no scale or signature.

Map from the *Antiquities of the City of Exeter.... 1677.* Almost a direct copy of Speed's 1610 map complete with numbered references it covers slightly more land, but without the detail of Hogenberg. Considering the fact that Izacke was a local personage the map is, in many respects, disappointing. The Haven is shown with a false island, and there is a wind mill in mistake for the crane at the quayside. In nearly seventy years since Speed's plan there has been no development.

---

[1] Printed by E Tyler and R Holt for Richard Marriott.
[2] Printed for Rowland Reynolds, next to the Middle Exchange, in the Strand, 1681.

**6.**                                                                                          *Hermannides 1661*

**7.**                                                                                          *Izacke 1677*

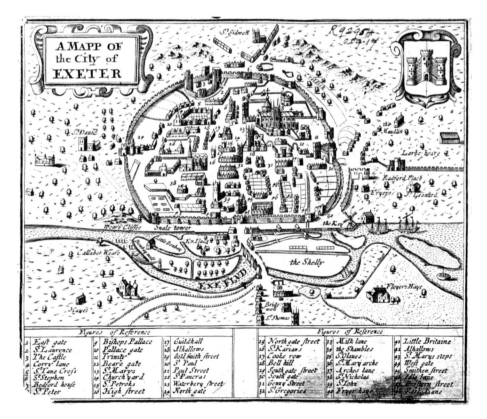

**8.    Ichabod Fairlove**                                                                                   *1709*

In 1709 Ichabod Fairlove was the first surveyor to produce a plan of the city since Hooker and Robert Sherwood (who produced a number of manuscript maps and plans) nearly 100 years earlier. This was the first printed plan produced entirely in the City. The engraver, Joseph Coles also illustrated William Musgrave's antiquarian works and the map was distributed by Edward Score, the Exeter bookseller. It included illustrations of the major buildings in the City and became the model for both Nicholls and William Stukeley in 1723 and remained the standard until John Rocque's survey of 1744 (see below). Only one edition is believed to have been printed and it was possibly issued separately as a broadsheet map.[1]

Title: **A True Plan of the City of Excester**
Size: 545 x 450 mm with *A scale of 1000 feet* (= 102 mm or 1Mile = 540 mm.).
Signature: *Ichd. Fairlove Surveyed Ios Coles Sculp*
There is a wreathed dedication: *This plan is humbly dedicated to Mr. CALEB LOWDHAM Junr. of the Citty Surgeon by Joseph Coles-*
Imprint: *Sold by Edward Score Bookseller over agt  the Guild-hall*

The map is decorated with four vignettes in the corners: the So. West Prospect of the Cathedral; the Guildhall; the Work-House; and the Custom-House. The left hand panel contains a column with a lettered strip wound round it *St. Peters Church foundd By K. Athelstan AD 932. 43 years Building* and is surmounted by the Bishop's Arms below two heraldic snakes twisted round two north points and the sun over the date *Anno Domin MDCCIX.* The right hand panel is similar but with the winding strip reading *Urb. Condit. Anno Mundi 2855. Ant Christ 1100.* The City's Arms are above with the snakes, north points and sun but no date. The scale bar is vertical.
The plan is drawn with north to the left and following the Hooker format shows the city from just over the bridge to St. Sidwell and from St. David's Hill to Wynard's Alms Houses on the London Road. Moving away from the bird's-eye view it gives a better shape for the city. It is a street plan with only churches and the Bishop's Palace drawn eye-view (but not the cathedral, shown with an internal plan). Principal buildings are either titled or numbered to the reference key. The Cathedral gates, the Great Conduit and the Alms Houses are shown. Of special note are the Shambles and the Bridewell in Goldsmiths Street, the Guildhall on High Street and the arch at the bottom of Key Lane. The serge industry is expanding: Rack Lane (11), illustrated on all maps so far, is identifiable but so, too, is the serge market with its stalls in Southgate Street (17), and there are racks set up at all points west of the city with Shilhay now covered[2]. Houses are shown diagrammatically and far too small: for example, some 13 houses are shown on the east side of Cook Row, in Southgate Street, as against the 8 in Hooker's plan of the city. The crane (Izacke's wind mill) has gone from the quay. Note the spelling of Bunny for Bunhay and Paree for Paris (Street). Lethbridge's Alms Houses (1668) in St. James Street are shown.
It is interesting to compare this with the following two entries (Nicholls and Stukeley) as it clearly was the model from which they both worked.

---

[1] Copies at DRO and WSL.
[2] To the eye it actually looks as though there are  two Rack Lanes parallel to each other near the west gate, but they are, in fact, Rack Lane and Rock's Lane.

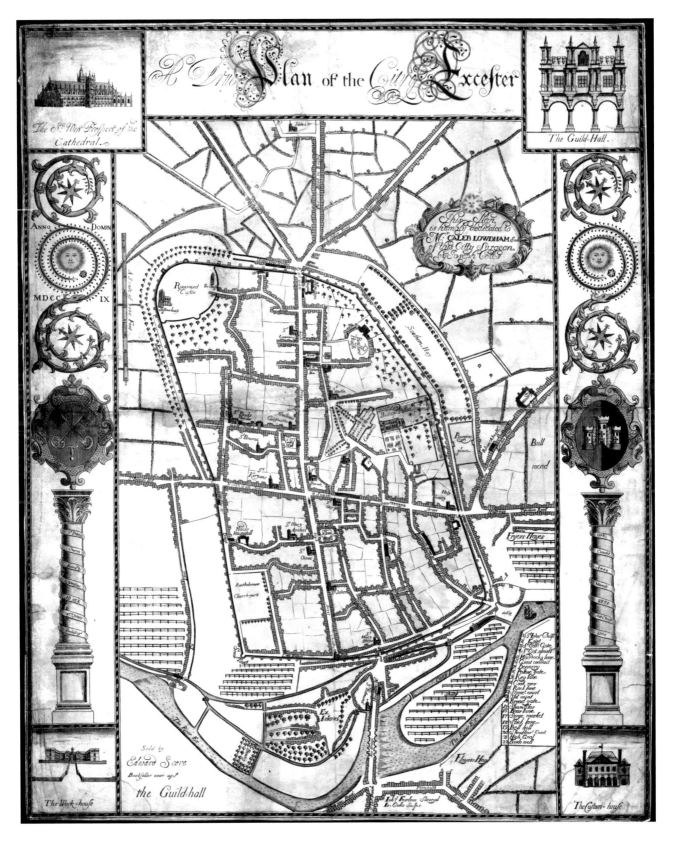

**9.    Sutton Nicholls**                                                                              *1723*

Samuel Izacke was appointed Chamberlain in 1693, an office he kept for some 36 years. He, like Hooker and his father before him, carefully catalogued and recorded important Exeter events and in the process updated his father's book, *The Remarkable Antiquities of the City of Exeter* (see 7). This appeared as *The Second Edition: Now .... continued to the year 1723, by Samuel Izacke Esq., the present Chamberlain.*[1] The map, engraved by Sutton Nicholls (fl. 1680-1740), remained the same in subsequent editions.[2] Illustrated on page 12.

**Title:  A True Plan of the City of EXCESTER Drawn & Ingraven by Sutton Nicholls**
Size: 254 x 162 mm with *A Scale of 1000 Feet* (= 54mm). Signature in title.

A faithful and well-executed, though smaller, copy of Fairlove covering the same area but retaining most of the former's features: the scale bar is drawn vertically; serge racks proliferate; no attempt is made to show individual houses; only churches and Bishop's Palace are drawn as views; and the important buildings are either titled or numbered but although the Guild Hall is highlighted he has forgotten to number it and add it to the key. Additions are the pecked lines to show the extent of the parishes and the inclusion of the Blue Maid's Hospital of 1708 (previously only Maid's Hospital). Nicholls has the spellings Bunnye and Paree Street and shows a different course to Genny Street and Milk Street. The title is in a simple ellipse.

**10.    William Stukeley**                                                                              *1723*

William Stukeley (1687-1765), physician and later clergyman, was a fellow of the Royal Society and secretary of the Society of Antiquaries, which he helped to found. He made long antiquarian excursions and was the author of both medical and antiquarian works. His *Itinerarium Curiosum* was the first of his books regarding his antiquarian tours, and the plates show England before the changes brought on by enclosure of the commons. John Michell (1984) writes: "As records of ancient monuments these have never been surpassed. Archaeologists still refer to Stukeley's plates and to the volumes of his manuscript notes and sketches, many of them now in the Bodleian Library at Oxford, as accurate accounts, often the only ones ever made, of monuments now vanished." The work contained 100 engraved plates and maps (some folding), mostly by Stukeley and engraved by Van der Gucht etc.

**Title: ISCA DUMNONIORUM 19 Aug 1723**
Size: 273 x 170 mm with *A Scale of 1000 feet* (= 31 mm).
Signatures: *Stukeley delin* and *Parker Sculp*.
There is a dedication*: Gulielmo Musgrave M.D. Gulielmi filio. Amico suo d.d.W. Stukeley.*

This is virtually a copy of Fairlove's but drawn to a similar scale to Nicholls' version above but is poorer in execution and it omits most of the lettering and references. He repeats Fairlove's houses but still without any accuracy. *The Key* (quay) is too far inland and note the quirk in the city wall occurs west of the north gate, not at the gate as in the two previous plans. Stukeley has decided to ignore the blossoming serge trade and hardly a rack is to be seen. Neither Bunhay nor Paris Street is named.

---

[1] This edition was printed for Edward Score, John March and Nathaniel Thorne who were booksellers in Exeter, and for Samuel Birt in Ave-Marie-Lane, London. MDCCXXIII.
[2] The 1724 edition omits Thorne's name and the date. Editions for 1731 & 1734 have a reset title page dated 1724 and added plates of the Guild-Hall and the Conduit. The third edition, printed for the author and sold by Score and Birt, 1741, reverts to the 1723 title page except for *Printed for Richard Izacke, son of the Author 1741*. A 1757 edition has a reset title page but worded as 1723 except for the date MDCCLVII. A slightly reduced copy titled *Exeter in the Seventeenth Century* appeared in Freeman's *Exeter* 1887, (see entry 53).

**10.**                                                                    *Stukeley 1723*

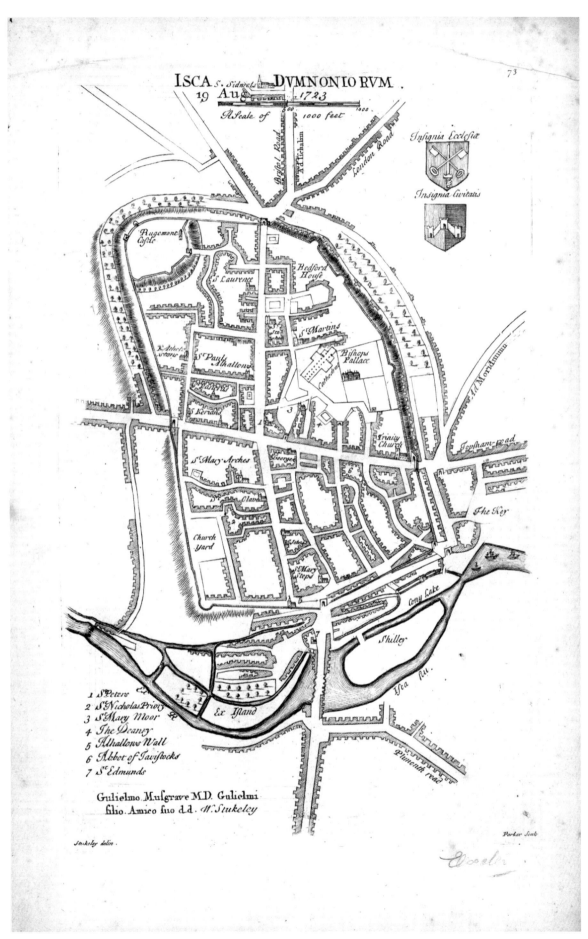

Over a period of just 25 years three of the finest surveyors of eighteenth century Devon were engaged in The City, the County of Exon and the County of Devon. John Rocque produced an accurate and probably the most attractive of all the printed City plans. Benjamin Donn surveyed the county and in 1765 produced the first one inch county map (B&B 44). And John Richards executed a set of manuscript plans unequalled, at the time, in their accuracy and their presentation (see Appendix B).

### 11.   John Rocque I                                                                                                *1744*

John Rocque (originally Jean, c.1704-1762) was of Huguenot extraction and moved to London with his parents in 1709. His brother, Bartholomew, worked as a landscape gardener and it is probably no coincidence that John became an established surveyor while making plans of great houses and gardens developing a distinctive style of his own. Best known for his large scale plan of London, begun as early as 1737 but not published (on 24 sheets) until 1747, he also prepared county maps (B&B 28) for a road book, *The English Traveller,* published in parts from 1743. Rocque must have executed the Devon map in that year. He maintained his French connections adding French titles to subsequent editions of this work when it appeared as *The Small British Atlas* from 1753. His maps of Bristol and Exeter[1] were the first large scale maps of provincial cities.

### Title: *Plan de la Ville et faubourgs D'EXETER*
Size: 745 x 1165 mm, printed on two sheets; there are five scale bars with one of 1M = 660 mm.
Signature: *R. White Sculp.*

There are two titles both in elaborate cartouches. The first is the dedication which reads *To the Right Worshipfull ye. Mayor Aldermen & Common Council of the City of Exeter. This Plan of the said City is humbly Dedicated, by their most Obedient Servant, John Rocque. 1744.* The City Arms, supported by pegassi, are above and the Bishop's Arms below are supported by five putti. The second title, the *Plan de la Ville et faubourgs D'EXETER, tres Exactement Leve & desseinne par I. Roque,* is above the five scale bars (¼ Mile, feet, yards, perches and chains) again above the note *Published according to Act of Parliament 1744.* Above this title is a small vignette of the surveyor at work, and below two putti hold a map of the British Isles, showing London and Exeter, while on the opposite side two more putti lie on the surveyor's books, one playing with dividers.

The border bears the arms of the livery companies. The north point has four wind faces with mast and sails behind the winds and ship parts and Neptune's trident are drawn below the first title. The area shown is from the start of the Haven to St. David's and from St. Thomas to St. Ann's Chapel in the east. The suburbs are shown along main roads, the space left being filled with vignette illustrations of the city: Exe Bridge; North aspect of the cathedral; the Work House; the Custom's house; City and County Hospital; City Hospital; Castle; West aspect of the cathedral; and the Guildhall.

The block plan is typical of Rocque's surveys, beautifully and accurately drawn, for example note the treasury building to the north of the Cathedral. The important buildings are shown darker, gardens are laid out, the fields are full of serge racks, and there are ships by the key and in the haven. The city is now largely built-up as are the main roads out from the city and nearly the whole of Exe Island. The churches, with the exception of All Hallows on the Walls, are shown together with the meeting houses; James in James Street, Bow off the High Street and Anabaptist's off Southgate. Other features are the alms houses, Davids, Hurts, Moor's, Palmers, and Wynards; the two Blew schools; both hospitals; the gaol and Bridewell, now outside the city on the road to St. Thomas[2]; the two Bowling Green(s), off Paree Street and Long Brook Street; and the Haven is shown correctly further downstream. This is the first map to show the suburbs in any detail but there is one interesting error: the churches of St. Sidwell and St. Lawrence have been interchanged.

---

[1] James Commin published a slightly reduced facsimile (460 x 730 mm) in 1911 (illustrated). This clearly has the imprint: *Reprinted in reduced facsimile by James G. Commin, Antiquarian, Bookseller, 230 High Street, Exeter. 1911.*

[2] A XIV century building converted in Elizabethan times as a prison (Bridewell) (see Jenkins).

**11.**

*Rocque I 1744*

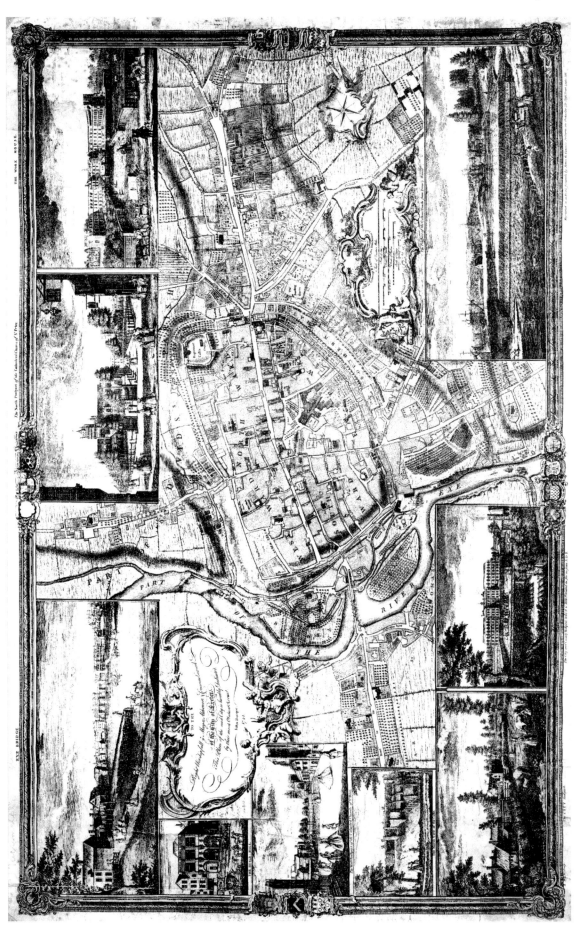

## 12.   John Rocque II (Andrew Dury)                                     1761

John Rocque died in 1762 and his business was continued by his second wife. However, in circa 1761 Rocque's son-in-law, Andrew Dury, printed and published *A Collection of Plans of the Principal Cities of Great Britain and Ireland with Maps of the Coast of the said Kingdoms*[1]. These were advertised as *drawn from the most accurate survey and in particular, those taken by the late Mr. J. Rocque, Topographer to His Majesty*. These maps and plans included a map of Exeter (sheet 8) but at a very small scale. It has been suggested that the plans were drawn by Rocque, but that he had died before Dury produced the collection. Inspection shows that the plan might have been copied from Rocque, but the lack of quality indicates the work of others. It is also possible that the plan was used elsewhere and even issued separately[2].

Title: **PLAN of the CITY OF EXETER**
Size: 91 x 110 mm, with two scales including 1M = 73 mm but no signature.

The title is at the top and the two scale bars, ½ mile and feet, are bottom left. The area covered is the same as Rocque's plan of 1744 but without the vignettes and with only a letter reference key to the principal buildings below the border.

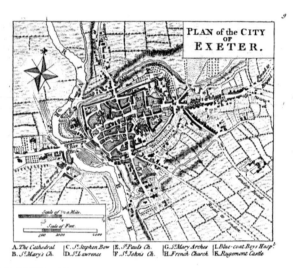

## 13.   John Rocque III (Mary Anne Rocque)                               1764

In 1764 Mary Anne, Rocque's widow, published a reduced copy of the 1744 plan, drawn to the same detail and in the same style. Was the large map too expensive to print, sales too few or maybe she felt that the map produced by her son-in-law, Andrew Dury, was too insignificant.

Title: *PLAN of the CITY of EXETER, Reduc'd from the large SURVEY in two Sheets by the late JOHN ROCQUE, Topographer to His Majesty.*
Size: 290 x 480 mm with 4 scales: Quarter Mile, Feet, Yards, Perches and 1M = 328mm.
Imprint: *Publish'd by Mary Ann Rocque, near Old Round Court in the Strand. 1764* (in the title cartouche) and a signature: *P. Andrews Sculp.*

There is a North point. The title in an elaborate cartouche adjoins a larger cartouche containing the *REFERENCE*. The four scale bars are below the border. The scale is just half of the earlier Rocque map and the area covered is the same except at the bottom which is cut off at Bull Mead and The Work House (established 1672). The spaces covered by the vignettes in the earlier map are shown as open fields. The Wards are not named otherwise much of the writing remains the same or has been replaced by numbers and the reference. Note the word *Exchange* written close to the Guildhall but upside down. The garden details vary but still show the Rocque patterns. The Theatre in the key (37) is that in Waterbeer Street, completed in 1734.

---

[1] London: Printed and Sold by A Dury in Dukes Court, St. Martins Lane.
[2] There are differently sized copies (one such measures 100 x 115 mm)

**13.**                                                                                   *Rocque III 1764*

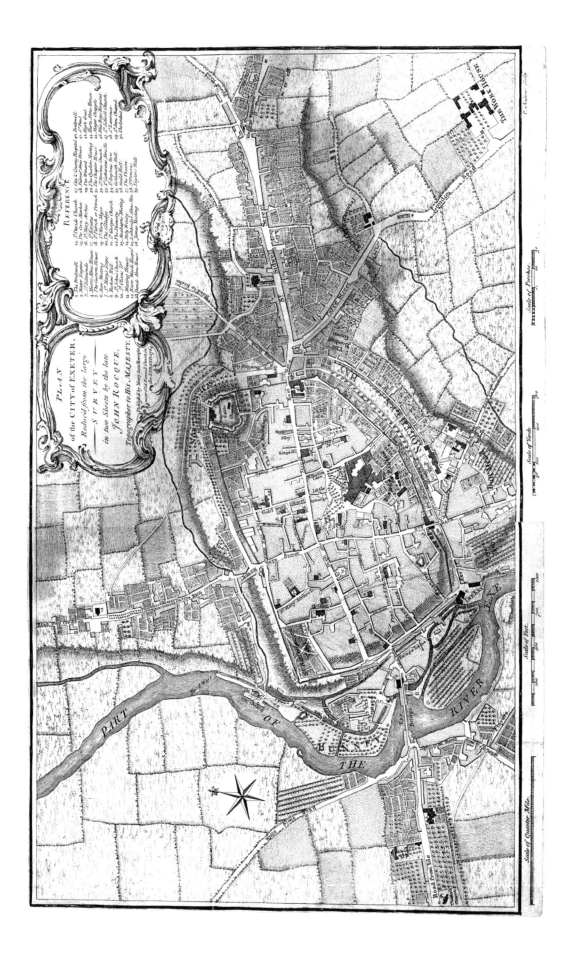

## 14.   Benjamin Donn                                                           *1765*

A Devonian, Benjamin Donn was born in Bideford in 1729. He was a well-known mathematician, writing several articles and letters for the *Gentleman's Magazine*, as well as completing his *Mathematical Essays* between 1756 and 1758. He was a surveyor and teacher of mathematics in Bideford before moving to Bristol. Also interested in tidal flows he published sets of figures for the S W of England. His large-scale map of Devonshire with its inset plan of Exeter is an important map for anyone interested in Devon topography in the eighteenth century (B&B 44). In 1759, the same year he married Mary Anne Wilcocks, the Royal Society of Arts (then known as the Society for the Encouragement of Arts, Manufactures and Commerce) offered an annual award of £100 for the best original 1 inch to 1 mile county survey. Donn and Isaac Taylors (Dorset) submitted entries but Donn was the first successful applicant with a twelve sheet map of Devonshire, engraved by Thomas Jefferys and published in 1765. The map of Devon was printed on 12 sheets and usually issued in book form.

Donn continued his interest in mapping (despite his experiences in getting his money from the Royal Society) and produced a map of the area 11 miles round Bristol (1769) and a map of Bath (1790). Together with his son, Donn published *A Map of the Western Circuit of England.*

Title: **A PLAN of the CITY and SUBURBS of EXETER** (inset on Donn's 1" map: *A Map of the County of Devon*)
Size: 405 x 470 mm with *Scale of Poles* (50 = 51mm or 1 Mile = 328 mm).
Imprint on complete map: *London: Printed for the Author and Sold by the Booksellers of Devon, by Mr Johnston in Ludgate Street: Mr Baldwin in Paternoster Row; and the print-sellers of London MDCCLXV.*

The City is shown on sheet 4 with north at the top, a scale bar and a key to certain buildings below. The area covered is from St. Thomas to St. Agnes and St. Davis to the Workhouse, with the city divided into the four wards. There are many similarities, both in style and information, with Rocque's large plan, printed some 21 years earlier, and especially with the reduced Rocque drawn to the same scale.

The plan is in block form with the principal buildings, churches, inns, alms houses etc. darkened. But, unlike Rocque, Donn makes no effort to show gardens, or countryside, only the serge racks. This does make the plan easier to read. Another striking difference is Donn's lack of detail and his depiction of secondary roads. But the reference to inns and the variant treatment of the Exe Bridge is noteworthy. Fore Street for the first time is named as part of the High Street. The new alms houses (1763) are shown. The Blew Boys School is called St. John's Hospital or High School. Note, too, the ruined alms houses, late Bonville's, in Rock Lane; and the Water Engine is clearly depicted on the river banks. The plan also shows the end of the *Haven or New Cut*, and the King's Arms Sluice. Development is still limited within the walls and to those main roads out from the four gates. Though there are faults to be found in Donn's survey of the County, the City plan is, like Rocque's, both fairly accurate and informative. The Synagogue is shown twice (number 12 in reference key): it is given as located outside the North gate but also behind St. Mary Arches. The latter building was only constructed in 1764 so Donn may not have known exactly when it was to be completed. Nevertheless, the map makes an excellent comparison with Tozer's survey of 1792 (see next entry).

**14.**                                                                                                    ***Donn 1765***

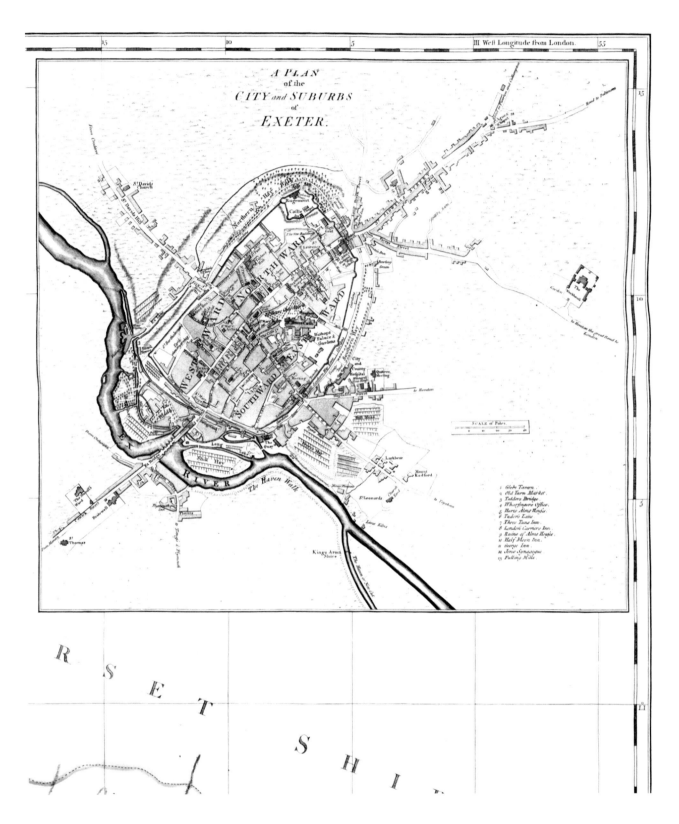

**15.  Charles Tozer**                                                                 *1792*

Richard Cowl, a prominent Devon surveyor had already published a survey of Plymouth in 1778 and was proceeding with a map of Exeter and a county map when he died in 1789. His assistant, Charles Tozer, continued with the survey and although he did not finish the county map he did complete that of the City in 1792.

Tozer was employed as a surveyor and drew plans of estates for the Palk and Kennaway families besides producing a plan and a map of Tiverton for Martin Dunsford's *Historical Memoirs of the Town and Parish of Tiverton*.

Title: **Plan of the City & Suburbs of EXETER**
Size:  269 x 335 mm with *A Scale of Poles each 16 ½ Feet - 80 Poles or One Furlong* (80 = 68 mm or 1 Mile = 272 mm).
Signatures: *Surveyed by C. Tozer* and *Engraved by Thos. Yeakell.* Imprint: *Publish'd by C.Tozer April 20th 1792.*
There is a dedication in a plain ellipse: *To the Right Worshipful THE MAYOR, Receiver, Sheriff, Aldermen & Commonalty of the CITY of EXETER, This plan is humbly dedicated by their most obedient humble Servt. Chas. Tozer.*

The title is on a rock pointed to by a goddess with a shield bearing the City Arms.  This is a plain block plan, similar to Donn, but with gardens and fields in the style of Rocque. The principal buildings are dark and titled. Churches are also dark and lettered with the key *Names of Churches &c* under the Bishop's Arms (note that U & V are exchanged). There is little development in the suburbs apart from the New Road or Howells Lane, house and gardens along Longbrook Street, the *New Gaol* for Devon County, the bowling green off Southernhay is now a *Racket Court,* and the *City Bridewell* is in Paris Street. The *Bridewell* in Cowick Street is named *for Devon* as is the Sheriff's ward opposite.

More serge racks can be seen: west of the river in Barn Field and behind the Devon Bridewell at St. Thomas; and on the city side of the river extensive areas such as those at Cullver Park (3 fields), at Bull Mead, and Fryers Hay (3 fields), at Bonhay and Shilhay (2). But the old city is no more and the feel of the City has changed: the New Bridge, opened in 1778, leads directly to Fore Street with a new opening through the walls and the resulting demolition of All Hallows on the Walls. Both North Gate and East Gate have gone. The Russell family, after acquiring a convent on the site in 1538, finally decided to demolish the house and lease the land to a local builders company who began to develop it and Bedford Circus is now half completed, with a road through the walls. The old theatre in Waterbeer Street remains but there is now a New Theatre (opened October 1787) in Bedford Street. The close New Cut breaks through the wall as does Maddox across the City and the Barings have built Mount Radford. The New Road (Howells Lane) now winds round the *New Goal for the County of Devon* (commenced in 1790 but not ready until 1794) but there are no signs of the new cavalry barracks to be built there (completed in 1792).

**15.**

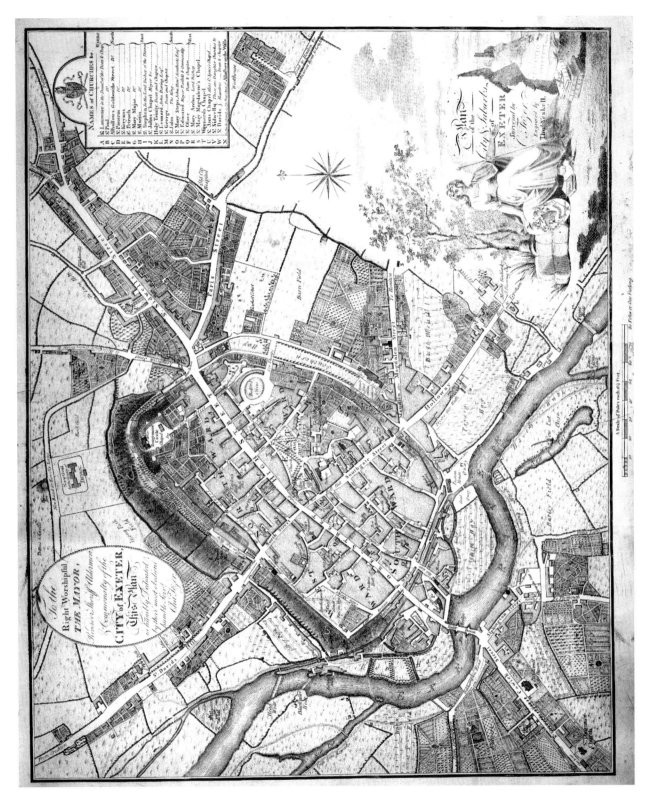

## 16.   John Hayman (Cole & Roper)                                    *1805*

In 1801 John Britton (1771-1857) received a commission to prepare the text for the *Beauties of Wiltshire,* the first county in the series of the *Beauties of England and Wales.* John started as a cellarman in Smithfield, then became an attorney's clerk and gave that up when he became interested in archaeology and had published his first work the *Adventures of Pizzaro* in 1799.  By 1805 he was writing about Devon and in that year he arranged with John Roper for the engraving of a county map by Roger Cole and a map of Exeter drawn by John Hayman, son of the Exeter surveyor. He went on to complete the *Beauties* with E W Brayley (1773-1854), a fellow antiquarian, and it proved a great success. It led to further illustrated county books of which *Devon Illustrated* was published in 1829, and *Cornwall Illustrated* in 1831 (and brought together in 1832).

The plan was also issued in the *British Atlas, 1805, published for the Proprietors*[1]. From 1810 editions appeared for Vernon and Hood and in 1816 for Baldwin, Cradock & Joy, and in 1816 *English Topography* by the Rev. J. Nightingale was issued by the same publishers. The *Curiosities of Great Britain ... London: Tallis & Co* (1835) also contained a county map but no changes to map area (only plate number or imprint etc., see B&B 67 for the county map).

Britton was one of the most productive writers of his time. An author of numerous books on the antiquities and topography of Great Britain, he was so popular that the Britton Club was formed in 1845 and a sum of nearly £1,000 was raised by a subscription for his intended autobiography.

Title: **EXETER**
Size: 220 x 180 mm with *SCALE 800 feet* = 24 mm or 1 Mile = 174 mm.
Signature: *Engraved by J. Roper from a drawing by J. Hayman* and *Drawn and Engraved under the Direction of J. Britton.* Note: *To Accompany the Beauties of England and Wales* and imprint: *London: Published for the Proprietors by Vernon & Hood Poultry, June 1st, 1805.*[2]

The Bishop's & the City Arms are top left and at the bottom there is a vignette of *East View of Exeter Cathedral &c.* signed *Hayman dd.* and *Woolnoth sc.* The REFERENCE table is shown in wards above the scale bar. A north point is shown. The plan covers the same area as Tozer except that *Holloway* is extended as far as *Parker's Wall* and the *Cotton Factory* by *Trews Wear.* The overall technique reflects Tozer's but on a smaller scale. The blocks are now more regular and are opened to show inner courts or gardens.

Outside the city walls: Bridge Street is named between the bridge and Fore Street with Frog Lane passing below; the notes Devon/Exeter are shown by the bridge; the western New Cut is omitted and a New Canal bypasses Blackaller Wear; the road from Bedford Circus has been extended and now passes through Barn Field (the crescent dating to 1800). There are numerous additions including Little Silver beside St. Davids, the two sets of Barracks off the New Road, and an Aqueduct to the City Conduits at the head of Longbrook (beside Lions Holt and the Ammunition Ground). Fryers Hay, previously full of serge racks is now built up with Graves Street and Colleton Crescent (only completed in 1805 after three years) but other fields are still dotted with rack symbols, even though their total area is dwindling, for example, Bull Meadow, between Holloway Street and Magdalen Street. Only one Turnpike Gate is shown: the gate opposite Parker's Wall on Holloway Street.

Inside the walls: the Wards have only an initial as reference; most religious meeting houses are shown as well as all the churches; the *Old Jail* (Tozer) is now the *Methodists Meeting House*; St. John's Hospital is called the *Grammar Sc.;* the Treasury, by the cathedral has been removed; North Street is widened by the old gate; and the chapel is omitted within the castle. The Quaker's Meeting House was built in Magdalen Street in 1806 but is already shown and is in the key. The Mount Pleasant inn on the river has become the Knave of Clubs.

---

[1] Issued in parts without a title page.

[2] Volume IV containing Devon and Dorset is usually dated 1803 but the map is dated 1805.

**16.**                                                                                               *Hayman 1805*

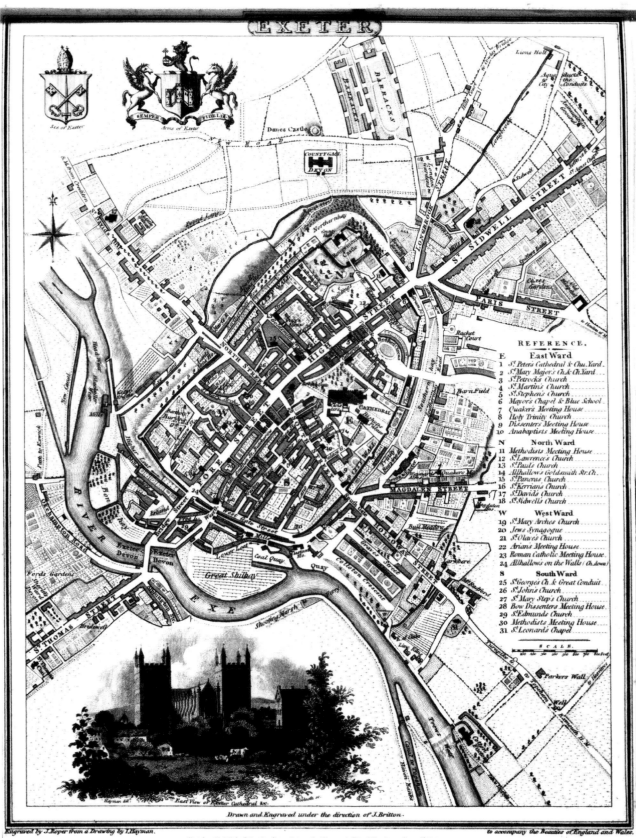

### 17. John Hayman (Alexander Jenkins)      1806

John Hayman´s original map (previous entry) was used as the basis for another map of the city included in Alexander Jenkins' *History of Exeter* published in 1806. The plan, though drawn to a smaller scale, uses the same technique as for Hayman's 1805 plan. There is greater emphasis on the suburbs so that toll gates can be seen and a number of houses are shown, e.g. Franklin, Barley, Haccombe and the two Cleaves to the west; Cowick Priory and Alphington House to the south; and Liverydole Chapel to the east. The area actually covered is from Littlejohn's Cross to the Tiverton Gate and from Exwick Mill to one mile out from Larkbear, the city boundary. The Exeter/Devon boundary is clearly pecked (omitting the northern part). Heights are hachured and Country Seats drawn in elevation. This map has more written information even within the city and appears to be more accurate.

A proof copy exists (see upper plan) before improvements, e.g. parish names include word Part or Pt, Franklin and Cowick Priory and a number of other country houses corrected, the Artillery Barracks have a new wing and outbuildings, and a picture of Mt Radford house replaces the previous plan.

Title: **EXETER**
Size: 205 x 235 mm with *Scale Quarter of a Mile* in chains 20 = 26 mm or 1 Mile = 104 mm.
Signatures: *Engraved by B. Baker & D. Wright, Islington* and *From a survey & drawing by J. Hayman.*
Imprints: *Engraved for Alexr. Jenkins History of Exeter* and *Published by P. Hedgeland, High Street, Exeter April 19, 1806.*

The broad hatched border has been enlarged for the title (compared to 16) and there is a North point. Whereas the list on Hayman's earlier plan (previous entry) included all religious meeting places this Reference Key only relates to the churches. The northerly barracks are now described and the new Artillery Barracks shown (bottom right); Hoopers Buildings can now be seen next to the Workhouse on the Honiton-London Road. There appear to be fewer buildings shown about Larkbear by Mt. Radford, and though Bull Meadow has lost its racks, there are further rack fields shown along Magdalen Street. The plan also shows nearly all the toll gates on the main roads. At Exwick a factory and mills are shown; possibly Mr Pim's paper mills which burnt down only three years later. Within the city the streets, most important buildings, the Guildhall, inns, hotels, Tuckers Hall, the theatre, the partly built crescent in Barn Field and even the markets are shown and lettered.

### 18. Anon / Alexander Jenkins      1806

A further illustration, also engraved for Alexander Jenkins´ *History of Exeter* of 1806. The plan is not signed and the lettering is of poorer quality than the city map.

Title: **A PLAN OF ROUGEMONT CASTLE as described by LELAND in the 16th Century**
Size: 157 x 104 mm with *Scale of Yards* 50 = 23mm.

The title runs across the top in a frame and a panel of References is below what is a simple plan of the North East Corner of the City showing the Castle Precinct, the walls and the castle buildings. Note the *County Goal*, just outside the main gate. It is interesting to compare this plan with the plan attributed to Leland included by George Oliver (entry 34).

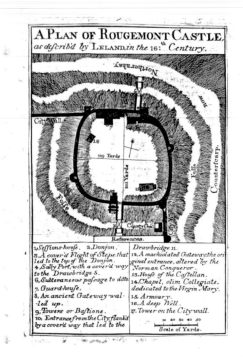

**17.**                                                                 *Hayman 1806*

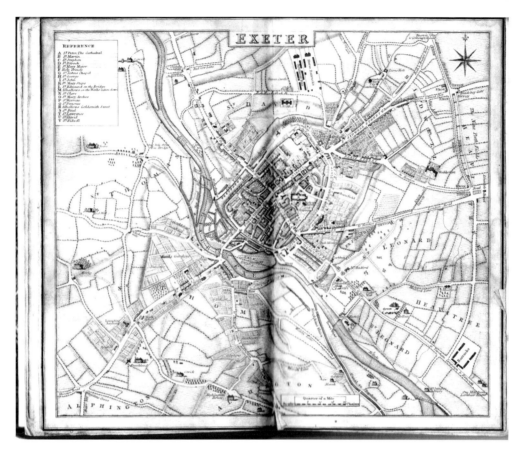

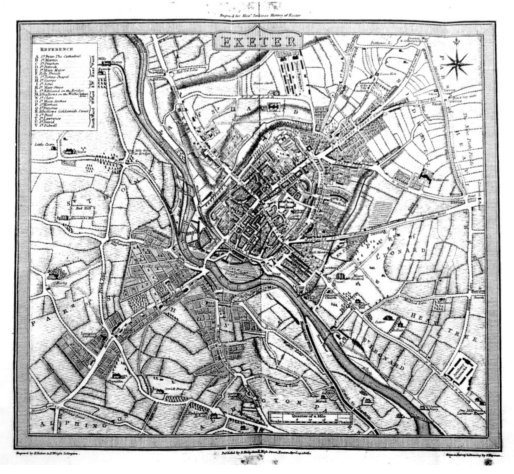

### 19.   *Mutlow (Daniel Lysons)*                                                              *1822*

H Mutlow engraved maps for Cadell and Davies to illustrate *Magna Britannia* by the Reverend Daniel Lysons and Samuel Lysons. This work was very ambitious and planned as an updated improvement on William Camden's *Britannia* (originally published in 1586 this was the classic volume on British history) and was produced in parts beginning with Beds, Berks and Bucks in the first volume dated 1806.

Mutlow engraved many illustrations for Lysons volume on Devon (Volume VI)[1] including a copy of Braun and Hogenberg (3), a county map of Devon (B&B 89) and three maps of ports/rivers. He also engraved some maps, including one of Devon for Marshall (B&B 60). Apart from this not much is known about him.

The *Magna Britannia* proved harder work than the historians planned and, with the death of Samuel in 1819, Daniel was only persuaded to complete Devon before the project was abandoned. In all only six volumes covering ten counties were produced.

Henry VIII's engineers produced many maps and charts as a preliminary to improving coastal defences including a detailed panoramic map showing the whole coast from Land's End to Exeter: a 'proposed' defence map of the coast, nearly 3 metres long showing inlets, rivers, defensive towers and castles and the principal towns.[2] The Lysons must have discovered the plan in the British Museum (as it was then) and made 3 plans for their volume on Devon. The part covering the Exe is described below: Mutlow's other two maps covered the sections of the Dart and Plymouth shown on this huge plan. Mutlow's Exe map was copied by later authors including Edwards in his *History of Exmouth* (published by W M Bounsall, 1868) and the Plymouth section reappears in works by R N Worth and M W S Hawkins at the end of the nineteenth century.

Title: **EXMOUTH HAVEN, &c. From a Chart drawn in the reign of K. Hen. VIII. preserved in the British Museum**.
Size: 390 x 270 mm with no scale, signature or imprint.

Copy of a section of a larger manuscript map of the western coast but only showing the Exe estuary as far as Exeter. Printed for inclusion in Lyson's *Magna Britannia Vol. VI.*
Chronologically, this is actually the second drawing of the city (as opposed to the castle, see previous entry and 35, 36 and 46) and, though only a sketch, shows the bridge, the Westgate, the Bishop's Palace, the Castle and the two Cathedral towers, both with spires, yet it does not show Topsham.

---

[1] Volume VI was published in *LONDON: Printed for Thomas Cadell, in the Strand, 1822.*

[2] BL: Cotton.Aug.I.i.35-39, it was part of an exhibition on Henry VIII presented at the British Library in the summer of 2009.

**19.**                                    *Mutlow  (Lysons)  1822*

EXMOUTH HAVEN, &c.
From a Chart drawn in the Reign of K. Hen VIII
preserved in the British Museum.

### 20.   John Hayman (T and H Besley)                                1828

Thomas Besley was born in 1760 and advertised himself as printer, bookseller and stationer or bookbinder and was listed in various directories of the time at Southgate Street (1801 and 1811); at Holy Trinity (1803); and at 76, Bell Hill, South Street (between 1816 and 1834). Thomas and Jane had 6 children including Thomas Junior (he became an independent printer in Exeter) and Henry who eventually became partner and successor to the family business. Few local printers published extensively but Henry Besley could claim to have been one of the most prolific of local publishers.

It would appear that the Besleys were in contact with John Hayman (see 16) and managed to obtain the plates which had been used for his map of 1805. They expanded the plates, added new title and imprints and included the map in the *Exeter Itinerary And General Directory - June 1828*. This was *Printed and Published by T and H Besley, South Street*. Issues of the directory are extant only for the years 1828, 1831 (no change to map), 1836 and 1839.

Title: **EXETER in 1828**
Size: 230 x 210 mm with SCALE 800 feet = 24 mm or 1 Mile = 174 mm.
Imprint and signature: *To Accompany the Exeter Itinerary & General Directory* and *Exeter, Published by the Proprietors, T & H Besley, Printers &c. South Street.*

Hayman's map of 1805 has been revised and has been extended to the east, to include the houses at the top end of St. Sidwell Street (e.g. Peerless Place and Salem Place) and the City Workhouse and Baring Crescent on the London Road. Coaver and Bellair (built by John Vowler, a rich grocer, in 1710) can now be seen. The Reference Key has been revised (e.g. Quaker's Meeting House is now St. Sidwell's Church) and turned into a scroll. There are a number of new buildings or alterations: the *County Bridewell* is shown beside the County Gaol and the nearby Barracks are slightly reduced; the *Proposed Basin* is shown near Trews Wear and the *Deaf and Dumb Institute,* established 1826, nearby has been added. Mount Radford has become a school (1827). The Racket Court has given way to Dix's Field (named after previous owner). A new canal has been cut at Great Shilhay. In addition the new gas works, built 1815-1817, has been included on Exe Island. This was situated in Archer Lane, between Tudor Street and Bonhay Road. Colleton Crescent, surprisingly, looks uncompleted. There are a few errors: Broad Gate has not been changed although it and 2 adjoining houses were taken down in 1825 for road widening.

The map was revised for inclusion in the *Exeter Guide and Itinerary* of 1836 (now only published by H Besley). The main change is that the reference key is removed and placed below the map; in the space now uncovered, considerable development is shown such as the New Road is extended from Bedford Crescent and back into Paris Street. Reference 35 is now the Friends' Meeting House, newly opened, at the new Friar's Walk. The new Queen Street is already shown as far as the city wall with a suggestion of extension but not yet named (opened 1837).

There are roads and houses between Magdalen Road and Holloway Street (not all complete). The North Road is new and winds from Longbrook Street out to the Bridewell and Gaol before joining the previous New Road and passing near the new reservoir (1833). Here it meets another new road which crosses Pound Lane and meets Northernhay Row near the New City Prison. The *Bristol & Exeter Railway* is now shown but without start or end: it appears from the compass on the banks of the Exe, follows the river on the northern bank before crossing both Great Shilhay and the river and ceases at the New Basin. The line was enacted in 1836 but not connected to the city until 1844.

For the 1839 directory the map was altered: the new road to the New City Prison has been deleted; the layout of the roads around Magdalen Road has been realigned (corrected) with a new road to join Paris Street; and new properties have sprung up between Longbrook Street and the New North Road. There are outlines of buildings at the New Basin: these were possibly supposed to be the new coal wharfs or the rival gas works built at Haven Banks and opened in May 1839.

**20.**

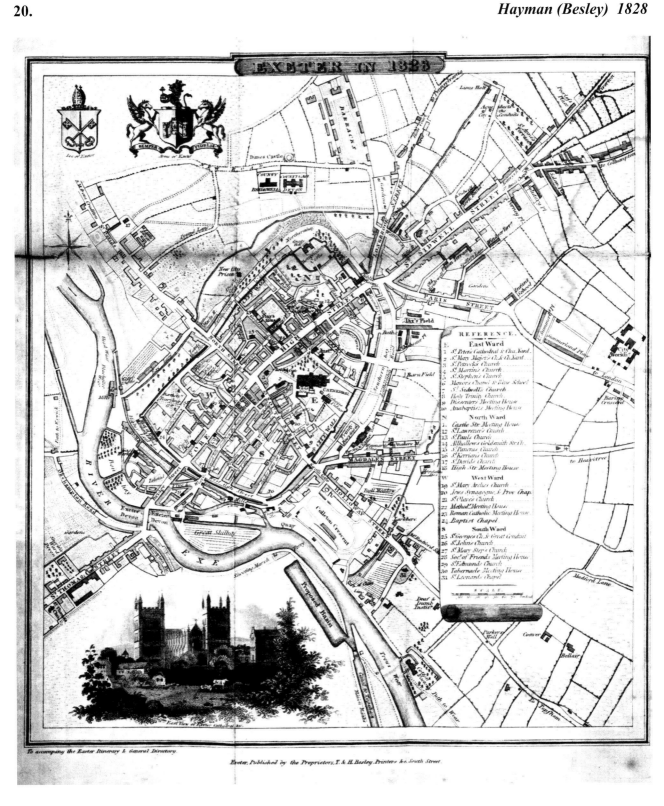

Thomas Hackett (fl 1830-1844) set himself up as a lithographer in Exeter after his marriage in 1824 and by 1831 he had become Exeter's principal lithographer working in Sidwell Street. He moved to Paris Street in 1834 and in 1840 founded his *Lithographic Office* in Magdalen Street. There he was joined by his brother William, a Captain of the Royal Navy, who later succeeded to the firm.

Hackett produced the three plans described here in connection with the improvement of roads and turnpikes and a city plan to show the old and the new City Boundaries (see Dawson I). None of the plans below is dated and all are from approximately 1828-32. They all include new, projected road routes which can be seen on later maps, e.g. Dawson (1832).

The company executed a great number of prints for Spreat's *Churches*. Thomas also produced a number of estate plans of local properties, e.g. plans of *Court Estate, Situate in the Parish of Dawlish,* the *Plan of Higher Hern Estate in Halberton* (1835), his *Plan of the Mansion House and Lands, called The Lodge* (Tiverton, 1835) and his *Map of Orchard Estate* (also Dawlish, 1838).

### 21.  Hackett I                                                                   1830

Title: **Exeter TURNPIKE Trust.**
Size: 290 x 450 mm with *Scale of Chains* (20 = 80 mm).
Imprint: *Hackett, Lithog Verney Place, Exeter.*

There is a north point, References (of distances) and a scale bar. The northern half of the city is shown from High Street and Fore Street. The plan shows the proposed new roads to the north of the city: Exe Bridge to Red Cow Turnpike; Longbrook Street to Belmont through Elmfield and Taddifield; a link road, joining both, through Townsen's Gardens. The City Prison, the County Gaol and the House of Correction (i.e. the Bridewell) are shown.

### 22.  Wills / Hackett                                                            1830

Title: *PLAN OF The City of Exeter shewing the Lines of Road Proposed by Messrs. Coldridge & Vicars.*
Size: 355 x 245 mm but no scale.
Imprints: *W. Wills, Exeter* and *Hackett, Lithog. Exeter*

The plan shows two alternative routes proposed: Vicar's line cut through the walls almost mid-way between North-gate and the Castle, joining the High Street south of the Guildhall; and Coldridge's line came south of St. David's Hill and South-gate ending mid-way along North Street. Coldridge also had a branch outside the city to the London Inn (formerly the Oxford) just outside East-gate. This branch followed the line of the 'west' new road, first shown in Hayman's plan of 1805. The end result was a compromise: Vicar's road with modifications at the City entrance and the branch line to a junction with St. David's Hill was adopted. Intriguingly, the plan predicts the building of the new basin and shows Exe Island as *Horse Fair* and Shilhay as *Coal and Timber Yards*.

Vicars and Coldridge had already worked together on a road between Wiveliscombe and South Molton circa 1824 (there is a copy at the National Archives).

### 23.  Hackett II                                                                 1830

Title: None but shows the planned new roads and a plan of the city of Exeter.
Size: 386 x 295 mm with a *Scale of Chains* (1+15 = 65 mm).
Imprint: *HACKETT, LITHOG: EXETER.*

A slightly better plan showing proposed Barnfield Road to join the London Road at Summerland Place (*now forming*) and the New North Devon Road (from St. David's Hill to Longbrook Street). Illustrated on page 17.

**21.**                                                                                   *Hackett I   1830*

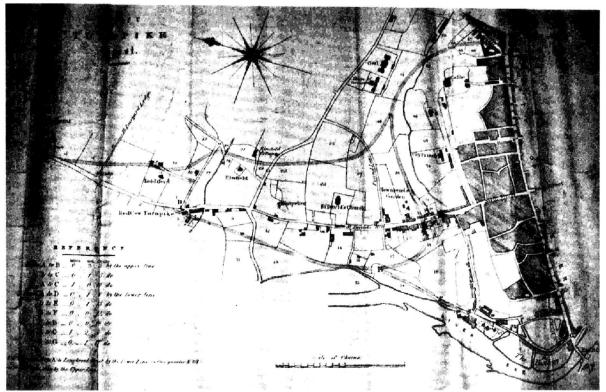

**22.**                                                                               *Wills / Hackett  1830*

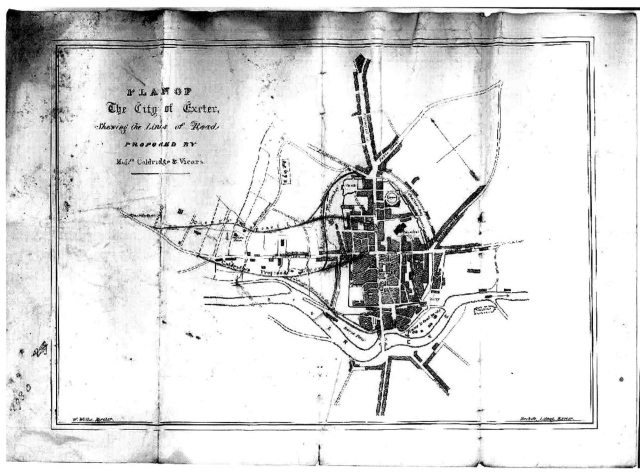

**24. Robert Dawson I**                                                              *1832*

Lieutenant, later Lieutenant-Colonel Robert Kearsley Dawson, RE (1798-1861) was the son of Robert Dawson, a Devonian, who had been active during the first Ordnance Survey of Devon of 1809 (B&B 74). R K Dawson entered the Royal Engineers in 1818 and worked in Scotland under Thomas Colby, Superintendent of the Ordnance Survey. Dawson prepared the boundary surveys for 277 county maps and city plans of England and Wales which were printed as a result of the Reform Bill of 1831 and related to the Boundaries Act passed in July 1832. The maps and plans were subsequently published in two volumes in 1832. This map was number 38 in Vol I of the *Plans of the Cities & Boroughs of England & Wales, shewing their boundaries as established by the Boundaries Act passed 11th July 1832.* This was printed by James & Luke G. Hansard & Son at their premises near Lincoln's Inn Fields, 1832.

Title: *EXETER from the Ordnance Survey*
Size: 250 x185 mm with *Scale of 2 inches to a Mile* (or 1 Mile = 51 mm).
Signature: *Robt. K Dawson Lieut R.E.*
Imprint: *G. E. Madeley  Lith 3 Wellington St., Strand* .

A simplified and enlarged portion of the Ordnance Survey to show the City and the old and new borough boundaries. There is no border, the title is top right and the North point top left. Under the plan are the scale bar, Dawson's handwritten signature and the lithographer's imprint. There is also a list, *Explanations*, showing in colour the various borough and parish boundaries. The map covers the area from Alphington to Pynes House and from St. John's Cross to East Wonford with the new developments in St. Leonard's parish along the roads to Heavitree. There are letters A to K identifying the new boundary markers. The wards are better shown in Dawson's map of 1837 (27).
Very soon after publication the local printer Thomas Hackett produced an almost identical copy with a new title and references, new compass, and with scale bar moved. All references to Dawson and Madeley were removed. Hackett did not always use the same engraving letters used by Madeley.

Title: **Boundary of Exeter** (centrally at top).
Size: 340 x 210 mm with a *Scale 2 Inches to a Mile* (100 mm = 2) (below text section).
Imprint: *HACKETT, LITHOG: EXETER* under the scale bar.

A two line border is added and the *Goal* (sic) is named. The definition of the boundary included in Dawson's report has now been introduced and written out in full at the bottom of the map.

*From the Turnpike Gate **A** on the Moreton road Southward along Cowick lane to the point **B** at which the same meets Stone lane thence along Stone lane to the point **C** at which the same meets the Road from Exeter to Alphington thence Southward along the Road from Exeter to Alphington to the point **D** at which the same is joined by Marsh Barton lane thence along Marsh Barton lane to the point **E** at which the same reaches the Western branch of the River Exe thence in a straight line to the point **F** at which Abbey lane reaches the Eastern branch of the River Exe, thence southward along the Leat to the point **G** at which the same is joined by the Brook which runs down through East Wonford, thence along the said Brook to the point **H** at which the same crosses the old Stoke & Tiverton Road near the Road to Mincing Lake Farm, thence along the Old Stoke & Tiverton Road to the point **I** at which the same meets the Old City Boundary thence Northward along the Old City Boundary to the point **K** near Foxhay's at which a Branch of the River Exe flowing through Exwick joins the main Stream thereof thence in a straight line to the point **L** at which the Road from Exwick to the Turnpike Gate on the Moreton Road is joined by a Road leading from Foxhays to Cleave thence along the said Road from Exwick to the Turnpike Gate on the Moreton Road to the point **A** at which the same reaches such Turnpike Gate.*

**24.**                                                                 *Dawson I  1832*

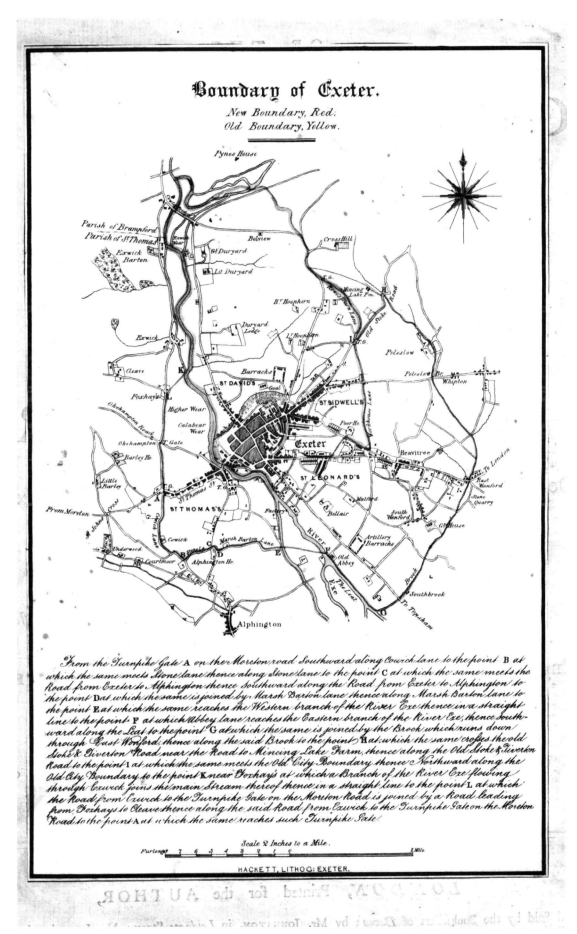

**25.   Richard Creighton**                                                    **1835**

Samuel Lewis issued his *A Topographical Dictionary of England* in 1831 (B&B 103) which contained county maps inserted at the relevant section of the text. In 1835 he produced a new supplementary volume *comprising a Representative History of England* which contained county and borough maps showing the electoral boundaries and changes following the 1832 Reform Act. This made up Volume V to the third edition of *Topographical Dictionary*. The *View of the Representative History of England* was issued as a separate publication in 1835 and 1840 with a total of 116 maps.

All the maps in this later work were drawn by Richard Creighton. The *Representative History* included Plate XIX – the county map, Plate XX – Exeter and Tavistock together; Plate XXI – Barnstaple, Tiverton, Ashburton and Dartmouth; Plate XXII – Devonport, Plymouth, Honiton and Totnes. The maps were engraved by the well-known partnership of John and Charles Walker who also engraved county maps.

Title: **EXETER** (The right half of the sheet shows Tavistock). Sheet Number: **XX**.
Size: Sheet 180 x 235 mm – Exeter 180 x 120 mm with *Scale of Miles* (or 1 Mile = 34 mm).
Signature: *Drawn by R Creighton*
Imprint: *Engraved by J & C Walker*

The Exeter half of the sheet has both title and north point. The map shows both the old and the new borough boundaries, from Alphington to just below Pynes House and from just east of Barley House to East Wonford. The map is essentially a copy of Dawson but at a smaller scale and does not reveal anything new.

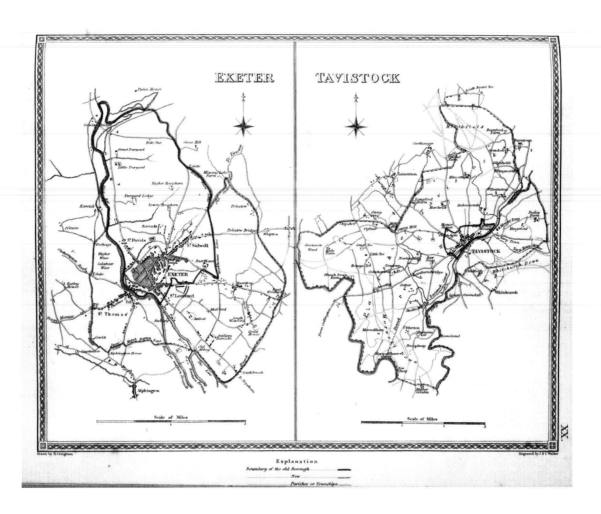

**25.**                                                                                              *Creighton 1835*

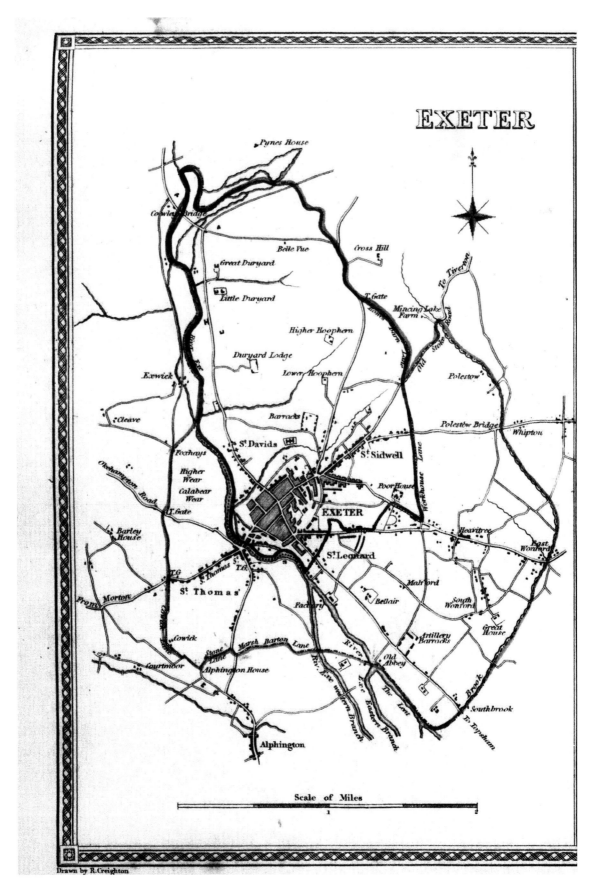

**26. Brown / Schmollinger**                                                1835

Little is known of W Schmollinger (*fl.1831-37*) outside his work on maps for Thomas Moule's *English Counties* (B&B 111). In an 1837 trade directory he is advertised as a specialist map engraver but little work of his is known. He had premises at 27 Goswell Terrace, Goswell Road, and later in Aldine Chambers, Paternoster Row. He may well have been the son of the Joseph Schmollinger and Mary Drew who married at St. Leonard Shoreditch in 1799[1].

In 1836 Schmollinger engraved an attractive map of Devon in a similar style to those in Moule's *English Counties*. The frame, typical of Moule's maps has columns right and left with two different and very ornate stonework patterns between. The map was published by R Colliver of Exeter of whom nothing is as yet known. It has Colliver's imprint, is dated 1836 and has been inserted into editions of *The History of Devonshire from the earliest period to the present by Rev. Thomas Moore. Illustrated by a series of views drawn and engraved by and under the direction of William Deeble.*

The *History* was issued as a part-work and was advertised in other publications.[2] The work was published in London by Robert Jennings, 62 Cheapside, and the first issue appeared on September 1, 1829. The first part issue (*about fifty numbers* were planned) contained the title page, two engravings and twenty-four pages of text which, apart from the extra title page, was the expected format. The two maps (Devon and Exeter), both promised in the initial *Mode of Publication* printed on each part, were then tipped in when the volumes were bound. The book was usually published in two volumes; the second volume having the town plan of Exeter, also by Brown and Schmollinger, and also published by Colliver and similarly inserted.[3]

**Title: THE CITY OF EXETER 1835**[4]
Size: 185 x 245 mm with *Scale of 1000 feet* = 35mm (or 1 Mile = 185 mm).
Signature: *Drawn by R.Brown.*
Imprints: *Engraved by W. Schmollinger, 13. Paternoster Row.* (right) and *Published by R. Colliver, Holloway Street, Exeter* (central).

The City Arms and supporters are centre bottom, the Bishops Arms bottom left and a North point, top centre. There is a small vignette in each corner: Exe Bridge, The Castle, The Guildhall and St. Peters Cathedral. The two references show Public Buildings and Churches (etc.). The area shown is from St. Davids to St. Leonards and from Cowick Street to Black Boy Road. Two new roads are clearly shown for the first time (but see also 20): the New Road from Bedford Precinct to join the London Road at Summerland Place; and the New North Road from Longbrook Street to form a triangle at Pound Lane. There is also a small portion of new road at the end of Paris Street. This map shows the line of the recently built Higher Market Street from the High Street past the prison and out to the New North Road. Rocks Lane has now become Coombes Street. All wall gates are gone as are the inner castle walls (except the Norman gate tower). Progress has been made on the new development between Sidwell Street and Paris Street and along both Magdalen Road and Holloway Street: note, too, the Gas Works on the Bonhay, the new City Reservoir behind Danes Castle and the Coal Wharfs alongside the New Basin. The key lists a number of newer public buildings such as the Athenaeum, opened 1836, and the Episcopal Chapel (1832) near Bedford Crescent. Only two areas remain marked as *Rack Fields*.

---

[1] Laurence Worms; Some British Mapmakers; *Ash Rare Books Catalogue and Price List*; 1992.

[2] Part XXXIX of *Moule's English Counties* (**111**) contained an advertisement for the various parts of Vol. I of Moore's work. See Tony Campbell; The Original Monthly Numbers of Moule□s „English Counties□; *The Map Collector*; Issue 31; June 1985; p.31.

[3] The work was also bound in three parts: parts one and two with the text; volume 3 being the engravings.

[4] The only known copies have been bound into *Moore's History of Devon,* with title page still dated 1829 but the county map is dated 1836.

**26.**                                                                                    *Brown / Schmollinger 1835*

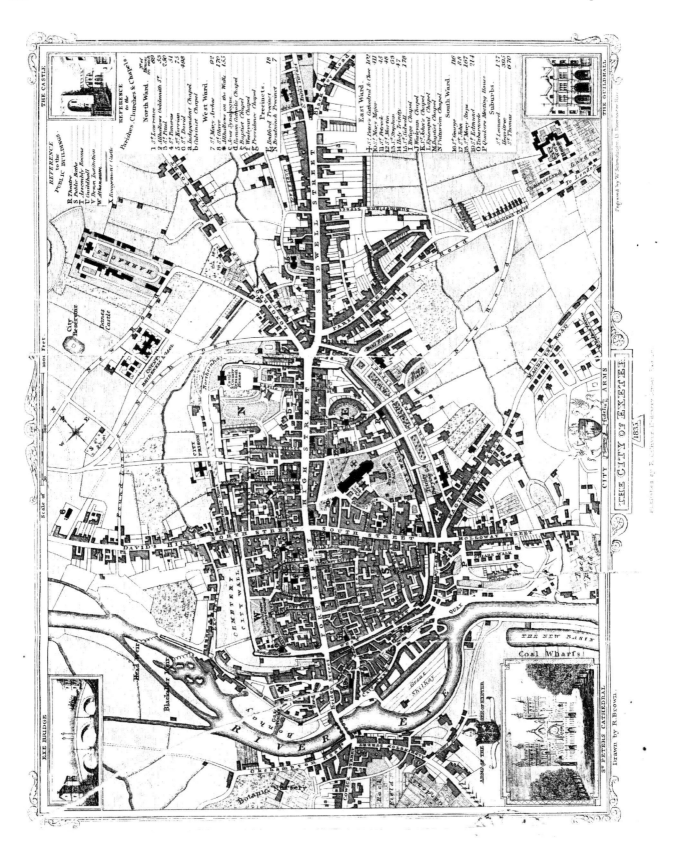

## 27.  Robert Dawson II                                          1837

As a result of the boundary reforms effected in the 1830s, Robert Dawson had already completed one set of plans for proposed boundary changes in 1832 (see 24). In 1837 he prepared new maps and plans for *Report of the Commissioners appointed to report and advise upon the Boundaries and Wards of certain Boroughs and Corporate Towns, (England and Wales) Parts I – III*. These included a sheet for Exeter which included two separate plans.

Reform was long overdue. Much of the findings of the revising barristers appointed to oversee the new Boundaries Act were based on the returns of the 1831 census, which showed a total population of 33,509. The Reform Act altered not only the electorate but also its size. In 1831 it was estimated that out of a male population of 12,683 a total of only 1,125 were eligible to vote. After the Reform Act some 2,952 electors were registered. In part this was reflected by the increase of the parliamentary borough from 2,400 to 4,600 acres as the maps show.

Title: **EXETER** *from the Ordnance Survey*
Size: 320 x 180 mm shows two plans. One is at *Scale 1 inch to a mile* and the second plan at *Scale 4 Inches to 1 Mile.*
Signature:  *R. K. Dawson Lt. R. E.*

There is a title, north point and two references (one to parishes and another to boundaries). A colour code is given for the wards and there are 2 scale bars. The two plans show the city as Dawson's earlier map of 1832. The smaller plan shows the enlarged borough boundary and the four outer wards (note the new Hooker's Ward). The larger plan shows the city and immediate surroundings in block form with the now two inner city wards Castle and Cathedral and the parishes although St. Thomas□s Parish is not named. Like Dawson's earlier plan, there is no border.

## 28.  W T P Shortt                                          1840

W T P Shortt of Heavitree, near Exeter, was a keen amateur historian and member of the Numismatic Society of London. He wrote two popular works tracing the findings of Roman remains in Exeter, *Sylva Antiqua Iscana,* and on the supposed druidical relicts, *Collectanea Curiosa Antiqua Dunmonia,* which also served as a second edition of the earlier work. The first contained a plan of Roman Exeter.

Title: **CASTRAMETATIO ROMANA ISCANA** (above)
and
**SUPPOSED FORM OF THE ANCIENT ROMAN STATION (OR CAMP) OF ISCA DUNMONIORUM** (below)
Size: 135 x 105 mm. No scale.
Signatures:  *W P Shortt Del.* and *Featherstone Lithog.*

The plan is highly speculative and based largely on the findings of coins, of which a great many had been found by 1840 when the book appeared. Shortt situated the *Quaestorium*, or paymaster's office, near Broadgate due to the number of coins found there. Other residences and offices are then assumed as a result of indications by Roman writers describing "similar" towns. When Dr Oliver wrote his history twenty years later, he completely ignored Shortt's work and Roman Exeter was reduced to two or three pages (see 35/36).

**27.**     *Dawson II  1837*

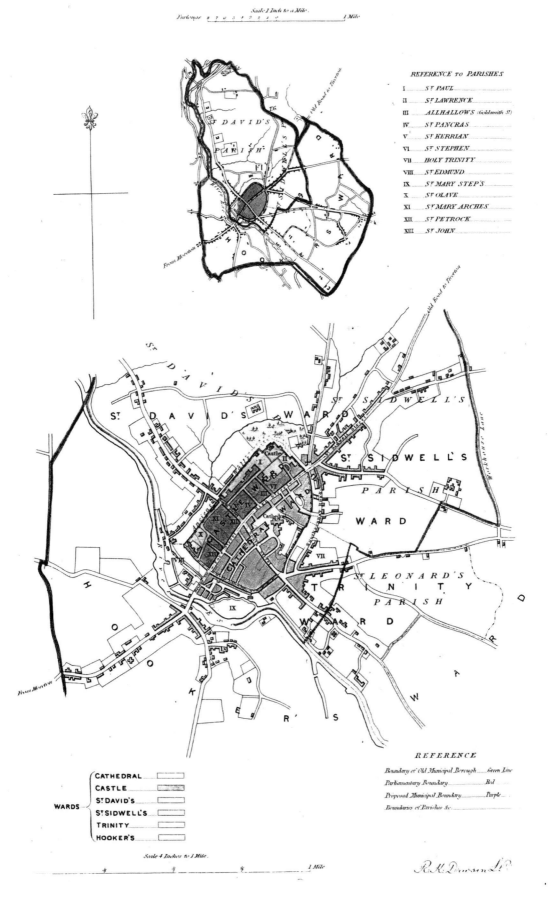

## 29.  John Wood                                                    1840

Nothing is known about John Wood. His name occurs only as an aside in Ravenhill and Rowe (2002) as no manuscript plans have been found executed by him. He must have been fairly well known or already to have established some sort of local reputation as he executed this map of Exeter and maps of Tiverton, Bideford and a map of Newton Abbot[1], all published about the same time.

This is a plan of the City of Exeter *from actual survey* – in this case for the Exeter Improvement Commissioners – by Wood. It shows ward and parish boundaries and accompanies a valuation of houses and land made in 1838 by Rowe, Cornish & Hooper. The population figure included of 31,344 for Exeter is taken from *Besley's Chronicle*. Also indicated are the names of the owners of land surrounding the city's built-up areas. The map is detailed and almost certainly used by later map-makers, e.g. Besley, as the basis for their maps surveyor (see 31).

Title: **A Plan of EXETER from an actual survey.**
Size: 675 x 805 mm.
Signature:  *John Wood, surveyor, 34, Paul Street, Exeter.*

Covering an area from St. Thomas to Polsloe Park and from Alphington Gate to Elliot Cottage the plan shows the higher and lower markets, Atwell's Almshouses and Victoria Park. Mount Radford and Clifton Road (Workhouse) are largely developed and Longbrook appears to be underground from the Iron Bridge to the Exe (this and the Shitbrook were partly covered in 1843). The buildings on the Great Shilhay include the Foundry replacing the woollen industry. The new roads have a slightly different alignment to previous maps.

## 30.  Standidge and Co.                                            1845

During the 1830s and 1840s a lot of time and effort was spent reflecting the sanitary conditions of the fast-expanding towns and cities and various reports were drawn up for the House of Commons on health issues. The cholera outbreaks in the early 1830s stirred action. In 1842, for example, a Select Committee paid particular attention to examining whether or not it was desirable from a public health viewpoint that cemeteries in large towns should be allowed to remain open. The committee's report agreed with the view of the majority of the witnesses that the city cemeteries were overcrowded and a positive danger to health. The report urged that no new cemeteries should be opened within large towns. In a further report of 1845 Thomas Shapter (see also 32) wrote a chapter, accompanied by a plan, to illustrate the report on Exeter in the *Health of Towns*[2].

Title: **Plans & Sections of the City and Suburbs of EXETER,** *Showing the Sewerage, the Division of the City into Sanatory Districts, &c.*
Size: 295 x 477 mm but no scale.
Imprints:  *Health of Towns Inquiry* (top right, above border) and *8voEd.* (top right) and *64/ Standidge & Co. Litho London* (bottom right).

The area shown is from St. David's to the Workhouse and Colleton Crescent to the County Gaol and including the lines of sewers such as *The Long Brook* and *The Barn Field Brook Sewers.*. The plan shows some principal buildings: the Cathedral, main churches, the hospitals as well as burial grounds and the water reservoir. Two sections cross the town: horizontally at a scale of 5000 ft = 94 mm; and vertically at 400 ft = 63 mm. Conduit sources (bottom left) are shown. Heights are noted on roads.

---

[1] The maps are at Tiverton Library, EWSL (photocopy only) and on show at the local museum in Newton Abbot respectively.
[2] Pages 205-266 entitled *Report on the Sanatory Condition of Exeter* by Thomas Shapter MD, published in London by William Clowes and Sons for HMSO.

**29.**            *Wood 1840*

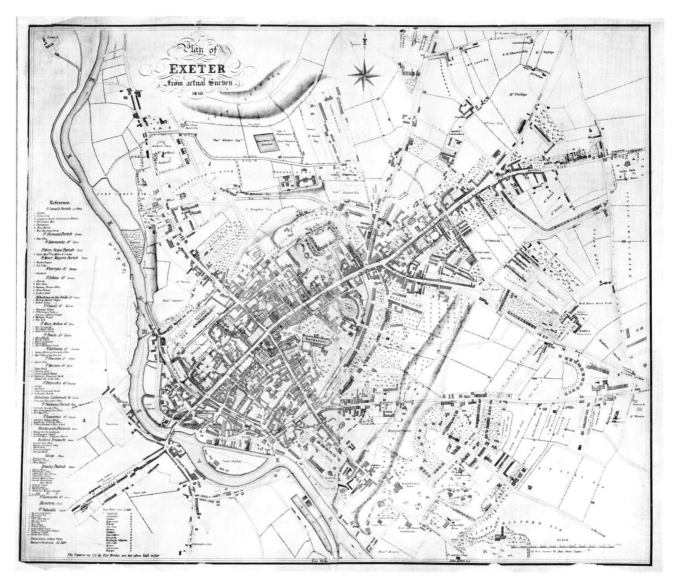

**30.**            *Standidge & Co. 1845*

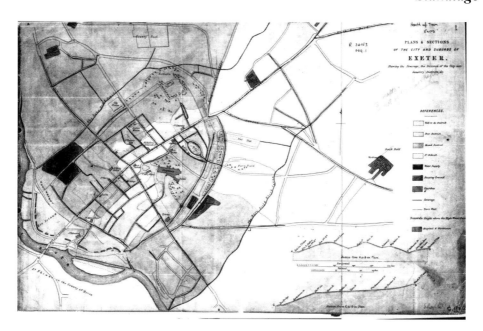

## 31.  *Henry Besley / J Warren*                                          *1845*

The first map associated with the Besley name is a map of Exeter which appeared in the *Exeter Itinerary And General Directory* in June 1828 (see 20) first published by Thomas and Henry Besley. Henry Besley commissioned a number of maps for his series of Guide Books; both county maps on one or more sheets (see B&B 122, 128 and 134) and a *Route Map* besides maps of regions, two maps of Dartmoor and his town plans. Henry's popular guide, *The Route Book of Devon,* was first published *c.*1845 with a *Second Edition* appearing approximately a year later. A map of Exeter signed by J Warren as surveyor, was included from the beginning. There were further issues until 1877 as well as handbooks of towns and areas with text extracted from the *Route Books*. The map was also used in Besley's *Directory of Exeter* from 1881 with continual updating and the map was used into the twentieth century (see Appendix C). The map was printed by a well-known company of F P Becker who lithographed a number of maps for Besley as well as some county maps for other publishers.

Title: **EXETER *corrected to the Present Time* BY J. WARREN, SURVEYOR**
Size: 230 x 280 mm and *SCALE* of 30 (chains) = 40 mm.
Imprints: *Engraved by the Omnigraph by F. P. Becker & Co. Patentees, 12, Paternoster Row* and *Published by Henry Besley, Directory Office South St., Exeter.*

Apart from the reduced size this plan owes much to Wood's survey (see 29) and almost repeats the 1840 map. The reference now focuses on public buildings and useful addresses and no longer includes the churches. This is the first map to show the railway as completed. The Bristol and Devon Railway Station opened in 1844 and is shown with two roads *To the Luggage Train* and *From the Train* at the Red Cow Inn. Mount Radford and Clifton Road (Workhouse) are largely developed. Other noticeable features are the Gas Works opened in May 1839 at Haven Banks by the Basin.

**31.**                                                                                   *Besley / Warren  1845*

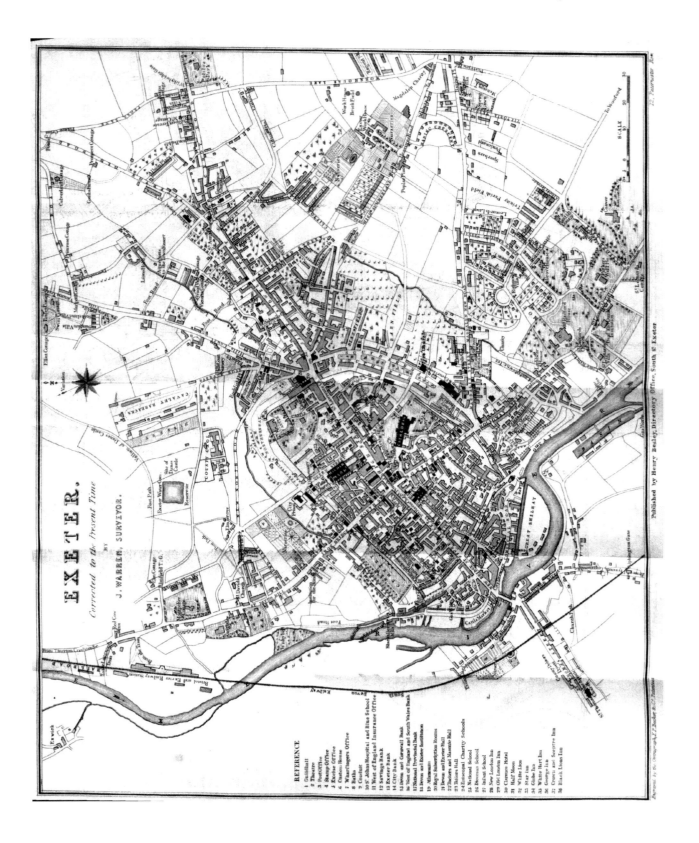

**32.   *Thomas Shapter***                                                          *1849*

During the three years 1832-34 over 400 Exeter and St. Thomas residents lost their lives in outbreaks of Cholera. 1832 was especially severe with over 1,100 cases reported and some 345 deaths between July 19th and October 27th in Exeter. In 1849 Thomas Shapter MD (elected to the chamber in 1833) wrote a report describing the cholera epidemics affecting Exeter in his *The History of the Cholera in Exeter in 1832* (published in London by John Churchill and in Exeter by Adam Holden, 1849). The disease showed that the population of the city was still distributed in the same pattern. The well-to-do parishes were those about the High Street, above North & South Streets, St. Martin, St. Petrock, St. Stephen, St. Lawrence, All Hallows and the Bedford area. The poorer parishes were St. Edmund, St. Mary Major, St. Mary Steps and probably All Hallow on the Walls, in effect the western part[1] Many of the great merchant houses had been converted into tenements with 8 to 10 persons sharing one room and some larger properties, still occupied by tradesmen and professionals, were now in the midst of brutalising slums.

In the last part of the 18th century the prosperous families escaped from the city to Dix's Field and the Barnfield or even further out to Heavitree. By the turn of the century Exeter had changed. The thriving industrial and commercial city of 1700 was now a supply centre for goods and services. The cloth industry had all but disappeared. This was all reflected in the Chamber where the members represented the professions and gentility and no longer the merchants and the guilds. The city as Newton wrote in the census of 1831 defined the problems and Exeter, relapsing into the status of a large market town, was ill fitted to deal with them.

Following the cholera epidemic the worst slums were pulled down and some 13 miles of sewers were laid. Plans were made to build 200 labourer's cottages and although they failed, they led to the *Newtown* building which started in 1839. In 1838 the commissioners raised £3,000 for the paving of the streets, partly for vehicles and pedestrians and partly to remove the open sewers. In 1834 the New North Road (from Belmont to the New London Inn) was completed and in 1836 Fore Street was lowered to improve the slope. In 1838 Magdalen Street was widened with the houses by the White Hart set back and projections removed and in 1839 the new Queen Street was built between Maddox Row and the High Street. By 1840 the new street pattern was in place to remain within the city for the rest of the century.

**Title: Map *of* EXETER in 1832 Showing the localities where the Deaths caused by Pestilential Cholera occurred in the years 1832, 1833 & 1834.**
Size: 177 x 205 mm (slight projection top right) but no scale. *Latitude 50°40' north* and *Longitude 3°41' west* are, however, noted.
Imprint: *Risdon Lith: Exeter*. Note: *To face Title page*

The area shown is from St. Thomas, bottom left, to Pester Lane, top right, where the border is broken to include the cholera burial ground which gave it its name. There are two references: above for references to the cholera such as soup kitchens and deaths in the three years; below for parishes and mortality rates. Interesting points are the shafts for water sunk off Sidwell Street in 1832; Long Brook runs alongside Exe Lane; and the new roads are not shown.

It is a sad drawing showing the places of burial and where clothes burning took place. Death rates were especially high between South Street and Shilhay with very high numbers in the area of Ewings Lane. The final irony: the Great Shilhay, site of the woollen industry for so many years is now the place where the clothes were burnt and buried.

---

[1]  St Mary Major had 388 inhabited houses but only 30% were rated and in St. Mary Steps only some 17% were rated: whereas 80% were rated in St. Lawrence and   100% in St. Martin.

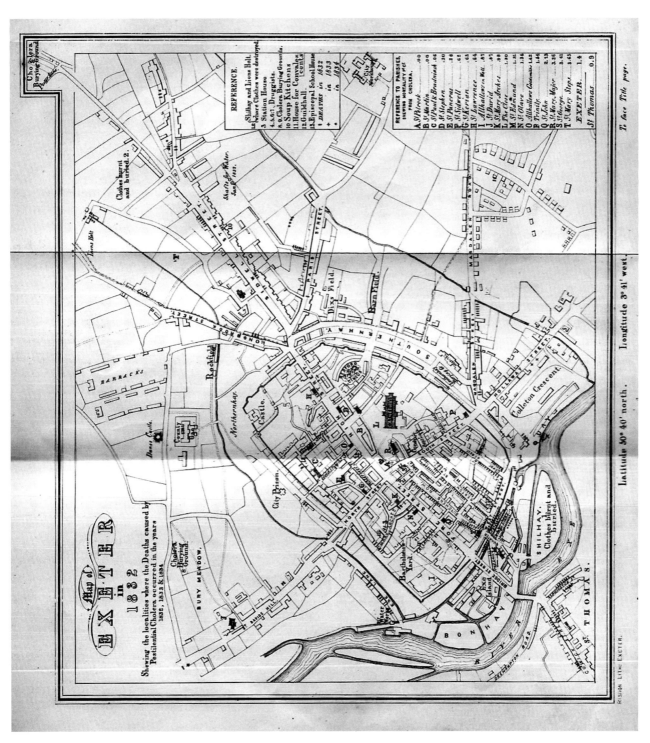

In 1850 Exeter played host to the Royal Agricultural Show from Thursday 11th July to Friday 19th July, 1850. This was a prestigious event, sure to attract large numbers of influential visitors and two guide books were specially produced for the meeting. There were two main show grounds and the meeting was expected to attract between five and six thousand members.

### 33.   Jewitt – Agricultural Show I                                              1850

Llewellynn Jewitt (1816-1886) was a prolific writer of topographical works and an expert on coins and ceramics. He wrote biographies (e.g. of Josiah Wedgwood), edited magazines (e.g. *The Reliquary*) and tourist guides to other counties, including Derbyshire for A & C Black.

In 1850 he wrote a guide to Exeter for the Royal Agricultural Society of England which was published to coincide with the event, *Royal Agricultural Society of England, 1850 ---The Hand-Book of Exeter . . . and a programme . . . by Llewllynn Jewitt . . . Exeter Henry John Wallis, High Street . . . MDCCCL.* This was Jewitt's fifth guide to the annual shows and the publishing schedule must have been tight as the Preface is dated July 1st, 1850. The volume included an extra plan of the show yards signed by Jewitt (L Jewitt Delt) and printed by Maddock & Balderston of Plymouth. Two further works by Jewitt on Plymouth contained maps: The *Illustrated Handbook* appeared in 1865; and Jewitt's own *History of Plymouth* of 1873, initially started to supplement the notes left by Edward Nettleton on his death, contained two facsimiles of earlier maps of Plymouth by Wenceslas Hollar and the Lysons (c.f.). He drew a plan of Exeter Cathedral for Murray's guide to Devon and Cornwall.

Title: **PLAN of the *CITY OF* EXETER.  LLEWELLYN JEWITT. 1850**.
Size: 310 x 220 mm but no scale.
Imprints: *Published by H. J. Wallis, Exeter, and R. Lidstone, Plymouth* and below the title *Maddock & Balderston, Lithographers, 17, Bedford St.  Plymouth.*

North is unusually to the bottom giving a turned look to the city. It is an open street plan from St. David's Railway Station (Red Cow Village) to Topsham Barracks and from St. Thomas to Sidwell Street. Primarily drawn for visitors, the plan naturally illustrates the show yards east of Mount Radford, next to Veitch's Nursery, and most of the inns and hotels. Noteworthy inclusions are St. Thomas's Union Workhouse, St. Thomas' station, and the Cattle Market just west of the bridge.

### 34.   Besley – Agricultural Show II                                            1850

Not to be outdone, Henry Besley produced his own guide for visitors to the prestigious show. Besley dedicated the guide to the President etc. of the Royal Agricultural Society, and this Preface is also dated July, 1850. It would appear that Jewitt had better informed sources: Besley had to include an Erratum slip to notify a change of caterer. Instead of Mrs Murch, a local confectioner, the gala dinner was provided by M Soyer of London.

Title: **EXETER ROYAL AGRICULTURAL SOCIETY'S MEETING 1850**
Size: 230 x 275 mm with no scale but with *Plan of Show Yard*.

The border is cut to make space for a *Plan of Show Yard* to be included. The map is orientated with the river from left to right; it shows area from Railway Station (St. David's) to Victoria Terrace and from St. Thomas Station to St. Agnes road junction. Drawn for the show, the Yard is clearly shown (by Veitch's Nursery). Two notes for show visitors indicate *To the Heavy Soil trial field* and *To the light soil trial field* (top). Both City Markets are shown. As on his map of the city for the *Route Book*, both Pince's Nursery and Veitch's Nursery are shown in the borders. Compared to Jewitt's map, above, this is a disappointing plan not up to Besley's normal standard: churches and chapels are listed in the key with only nine public buildings, and no hotels or inns are identified.

**33.**                                                                                        *Jewitt 1850*

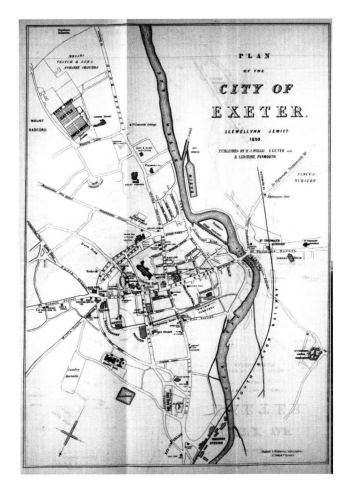

**34.**                                                                                        *Besley 1850*

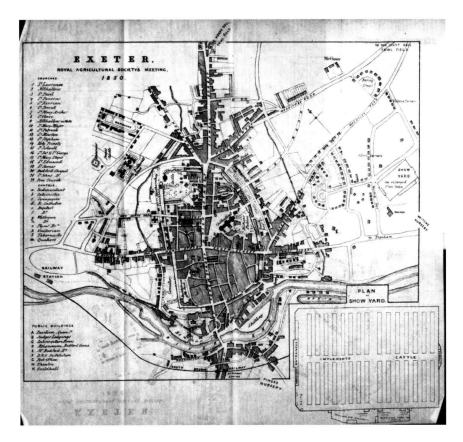

### 35.  George Oliver / John Leland                                    *1850 (1600)*

The Reverend George Oliver was both Catholic priest and Exeter historian. He was born at Newington, Surrey in 1781 and was promoted to holy orders and moved to Exeter to the mission of the Society of Jesus at St. Nicholas in 1807. He retired in 1851 but continued to live in the priory until his death in 1861. He wrote numerous works on the history of Devon, the church and the catholic faith in the west. Probably while researching for material for a second edition of his *History of Exeter* (first published 1821) he came across two early plans of the castle which he then included in an essay in *The Archaeological Journal* of June 1850[1]. The first was a manuscript plan (the original 480 x 480 mm) in the British Library which was for a long time thought to be by John Leland, the antiquarian and poet who visited Exeter in 1542.[2]

Title: **GROUND PLAN OF EXETER CASTLE** above plan and below **From an Original Survey in the reign of Henry VIII Preserved in the British Museum.**
Size: 110 x 115 mm. No signature. An indication of scale is shown by 300 paces across courtyard.

It shows the old Norman entry, closed up in late medieval time, as the *Ould Port*, and beside it *ye latter port*, where Castle Street ends today. Opposite, across the court, are the *ould* and *latter* sally ports. It shows the escarpment and the ditch, but it shows no buildings within the court and only suggests King John's bastion and Athelstan's tower.

### 36.  George Oliver / John Norden                                    *1850 (1617)*

John Norden (1548-1625), surveyor and topographer, produced the first complete series of county histories and invented the triangular distance table (*Intended Guyde for English Travailers* in 1625). In 1600 he was appointed to survey the crown's forests in Devon (and other counties) and surveyed those areas c.1608. As surveyor of the King's castles (appointed 1612) Norden surveyed Exeter castle in 1615 or 1617 (when James I made over the manorial rights of the Duchy of Lancaster and Cornwall to his 'dearly beloved Charles'). The survey was presumably drawn to settle the actual castle boundaries, and made under the instruction of Sir James Fullerton, Surveyor General.

Title: **FACSIMILE PLAN OF THE CASTLE PRECINCT, EXETER** and below **MADE BY NORDEN IN 1617, AND ATTACHED TO HIS SURVEY. ADDL MSS BRITISH MUSEUM No. 6027.**
Size: nominally 170 x 205 mm. There is no scale.
Signatures: *P. H. De la Motte, del.* (bottom left) and *J. H. le Keux, sc.* (bottom right).

Plain sketch of castle area with the border broken at the top for a small triangular piece of the Castle Hill. Letters A – K as references but which are not explained on the map sheet.
This plan was included by Oliver in two of his writings: it appeared first in *The Archaeological Journal* of June 1850 (see above, illustrated opposite); and it was reissued with the reference key (see opposite) in his *History of Exeter* of 1861 with letter L added, signatures replaced by that of *Geo. G. Palmer, Lith, Exeter* and everything in title after date deleted. The plan was also copied for W M Bounsall☐s *Exmouth and its Neighbourhood* (1868) with small variations. Bounsall's plan has title *John Norden's Plan of Exceter Castle and Parte of the Citie of Exceter 1617* (upper case) and is signed by *Day & Son (Limited) Lith.*

---

[1] *The Archaeological Journal for the Encouragement and Prosecution into the Arts and Monuments of the Early and Middle Ages* published by the Archaeological Institute of Great Britain and Ireland June 1850 as part of Volume VII.
[2] It was described as "Temp. Henry VIII" but Peter Barber of the Map Library has suggested a date closer to 1600 based on the style of hand-writing (i.e. 50 years after Leland's death).

**35.**                                                                    *Oliver / Leland 1850*

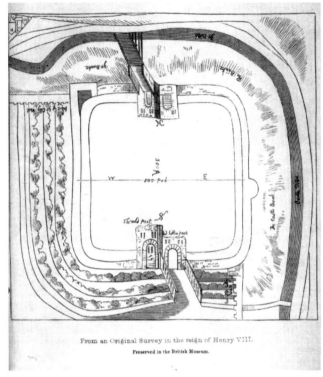

From an Original Survey in the reign of Henry VIII.

Preserved in the British Museum.

**36.**                                                                    *Oliver / Norden 1850*

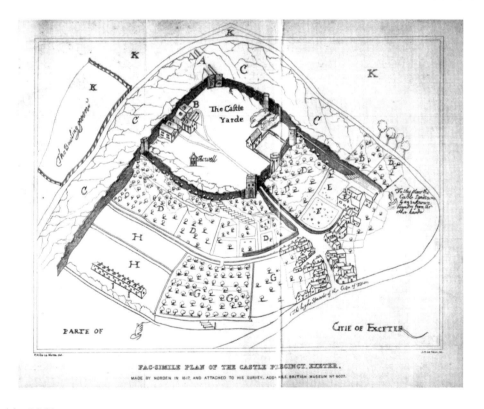

FAC-SIMILE PLAN OF THE CASTLE PRECINCT, EXETER.

MADE BY NORDEN IN 1617, AND ATTACHED TO HIS SURVEY. ADD¹ MSS. BRITISH MUSEUM Nº 6027.

Key as added in 1861:

A  The old draw-bridge over the ditch.
B  The Assizes & Sessions house built about 1624 (sic)   C  The outer ditch of the Castle
D  The inner Castle ditch converted into Gardens.         E  A garden
F  The old Prison, removed about 1796.                    G  Orchards & Gardens
H  A part of the Castle Precincts                         I  Mr Manwayrings new houses (1617)
K  The Castle Hill                                        L  St. Mary's Chapel

### 37.   *Featherstone & Co. I*                                                    *1852*

The Featherstone company of lithographers and printers produced two maps of Exeter in the 1850s (see also 40). William Charleton Featherstone was born circa 1794-95 in Plymouth and died 3rd February 1858 in Exeter. He married Jane and they had one son, Samuel, but it was Jane who registered William's death and it was probably she who announced the sale of her late husband's business to John Pollard in the *Exeter Flying Post* of 18th March of the same year. William worked from a large number of addresses and he is listed at 67 Fore Street in Pigot's 1822 directory and under the *Weekly Times Office* 1828. As early as 1825 he printed a broadsheet on the proposed railway to Exeter (printer to J Godfrey). Between September 1832 and April 1833 18 issues of *The Western Spy* were published: the first two under Featherstone, the others by W C Pollard. He also published the *Western Times* for a while but severed connection with the paper to start up *Featherstone's Exeter Times* in 1836 which was not successful and ran for only four months.

Title: **MAP OF THE CITY OF EXETER, EMBRACING ALL THE Alterations and Improvements to the Present Period.**
Size: 445 x 590 mm with scale *Chains* 22 = 73 mm.
Imprint: *DRAWN, PRINTED AND PUBLISHED BY FEATHERSTONE & Co. LITHOGRAPHERS AND PRINTERS. 246, High Street, Exeter.*

A panel on both sides shows the 'Street List'. There is a scale bar and the City Arms. There is a note on population: *Population 1851, City of Exeter, 32,818 but including St. Thomas &c. 38,886.* Three panels at the bottom list the parishes, the churches and public buildings. One interesting feature is the 'cross' shape to the City Prison which reappears on later maps: Warren correctly showed the prison as a shallow 'H' shaped building.

### 38.   *Tallis / Rapkin*                                                    *1852*

The Tallis family were leading London publishers of atlases and famous for their illustrations of the facades of London Streets. Their hallmark was the use of elaborate frames around their maps often incorporating a wide variety of scenes.

Title: **EXETER**
Size: 230 x 305 mm (excl. frame) with *Scale of* (20 = 53 mm) *Chains or ¼ of a Mile.*
Imprints: *The Illustrations Drawn & Engraved by H Winkles* (bottom left), *JOHN TALLIS & COMPANY, LONDON & NEW YORK* (below central) and *The Plan Drawn & Engraved by J Rapkin* (bottom right).

Three line border with highly ornate baroque edging incorporating both the title and the Scale Bar. There is a North point and there are six vignettes surrounding the plan itself: Southernhay; Post Office; St. Sidwell's; view of the Exe; Guildhall; Exeter Cathedral. The county prison plan is a 'cross' similar to Featherstone's symbolised building. Nevertheless, it is an attractive map, clear and precise, and principal buildings are named.

**37.**                                                        *Featherstone 1 1852*

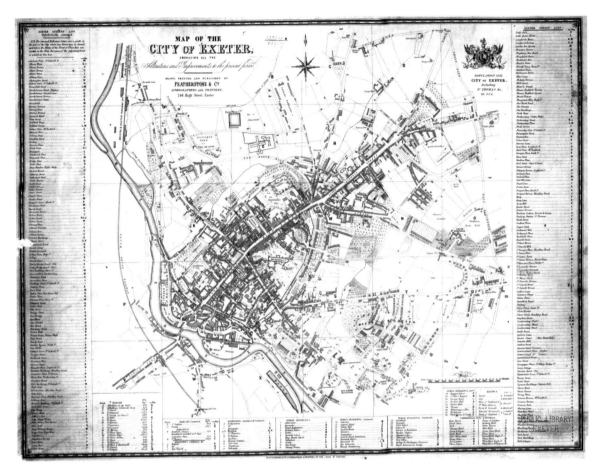

**38.**                                                        *Tallis / Rapkin 1852*

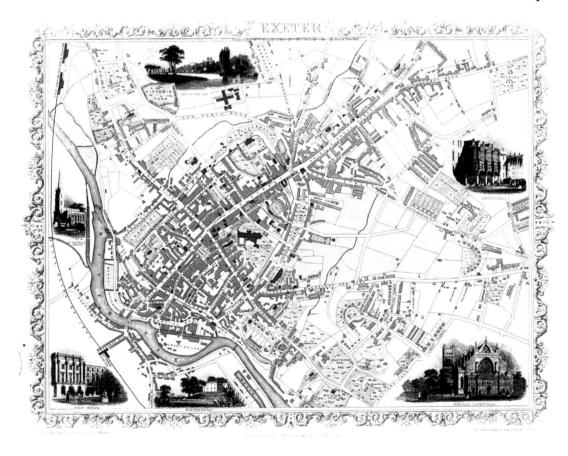

**39.    *Palmer & Stone / William Wood***                                              *1857*

Palmer & Stone advertised in John Billing's *Directory and Gazetteer* of 1857. They had taken over from Angel & Co. and advertised themselves as Practical Engravers, Copper-plate and Lithographic Printers as well as providing the usual odd assortment of services, e.g. wedding orders, maps, bill heads and cards *all executed on very short notice and at the lowest possible price.* They operated the West of England Engraving and Printing Office at 3, Waterbeer Street and were established in 1816.

In or around 1857 the present map was included in two separate works. A simplified version appeared in W William Wood's 3rd edition of the *Hand-book to South Devon, Dartmoor Etc.* with the imprint of *Palmer & Stone, Exeter.* A short time later Palmer and Stone published *The Hand-Book to Exeter.*[1] There were considerable changes to this edition: 10 attractive vignettes have been added and the map is considerably larger at 260 x 325 mm. The ten vignettes are: Exeter from Exwick Hill; Bury Meadow; Fore Street; High Street; Queen Street; Northernhay; Quay; Guildhall; Castle; and the Cathedral. An imprint replaces the signature *Engraved for the Hand Book to Exeter, Published by Palmer & Stone, Waterbeer Street, Exeter.*

The map was reissued in the third edition of the *Exeter Hand-Book* (circa 1863) with a new imprint: *Engraved for the Hand Book to Exeter, by G. G. Palmer, 3, Waterbeer Street, Exeter.* The map is slightly wider (at 350 mm) and the vignettes are repositioned with the Castle vignette replaced above the Guildhall so revealing the junction of Heavitree Rd and Magdalen New Road and *To Wonford* replaced beyond the road. The London & South Western Railway is shown with Queen Street Station and Longbrook ends at the New North Road. There was the addition of the *Agricultural Exhibition* which occupies the same space as the Show Yard of 1850, the adjacent note *To Wonford,* and the Free Cottages.

**Title: MAP OF EXETER *Corrected to the present time.***
Size: 260 x 335 mm with *SCALE Chains* 40 = 41mm.
Signature: *Palmer & Stone, Exeter.*

Plain three line border, title above the North point, the scale bar and the City's Arms have seated pegassi. The Reference Key is printed on the adjoining leaf: Public Buildings; Hotels; Parish; Precincts; Dissenting Chapels &c. Note the detail and the parks and planting reminiscent of Rocque□s and Hayman´s plans.

Although the Tallis map a few years earlier is very attractive (and is usually found hand-coloured) this map is a very well executed plan and has far more developments given that it was engraved only about five years later.

The map was used again in 1872 in the fourth *Handbook to Exeter.* The Arms and Northernhay have changed places as have the Guildhall and the Castle. Development is shown east of Workhouse Lane and note the new brick fields south of Black Boy Road. The Agricultural Exhibition has been erased, the Militia Barracks are shown on Cowick Street, the county gaol and the reservoirs are reshaped. Note the development by Bury Meadow and Longbrook has disappeared. Circa 1877 new imprints appear: *Entd. At Stationers Hall – Engraved & Printed by E.S.A.Robinson & Co. Bristol; for the Handbook to Exeter.* About this time the county prison changes from the cross shape to the H form. A *New Edition* of the *Hand-Book*, possibly published by W Wood again, appeared circa 1881 (illustrated) with no imprint and some minor changes: city crest simplified; Rougemont Hotel replaces the City Prison; and there are new houses opposite Bury Meadow.

---

[1] The text of both was written about 1855 but as the vignettes were retained in later issues it seems probable that Wood´s *Hand-Book* appeared first.

**39.**

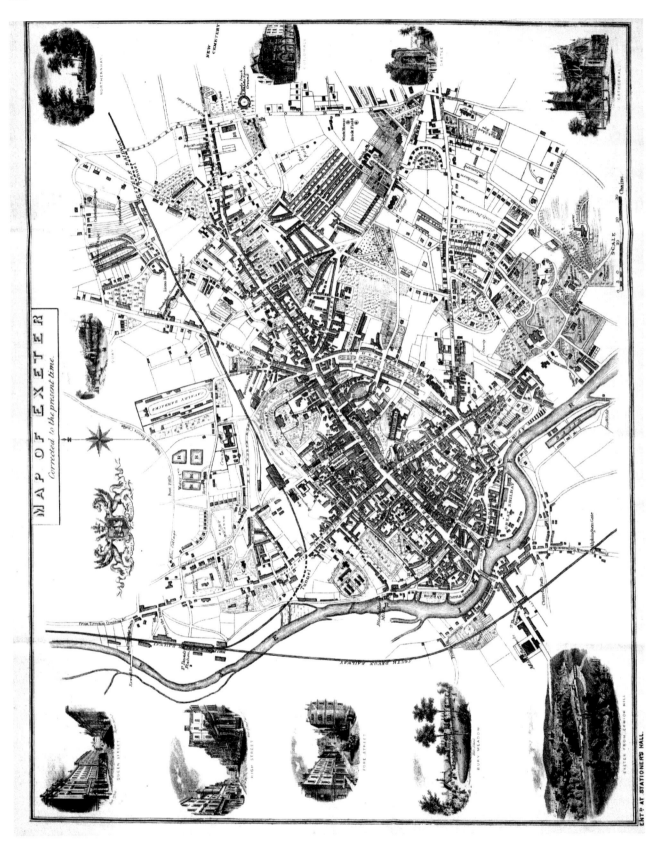

**40.    *Featherstone & Co. II***                                                                        *1858*

The actual dating of this smaller map by Featherstone is not known but seems to be a few years later than the large plan executed in 1850 (see 37 above). On the one hand the reservoir is still portrayed as a single basin although two filter beds had been added in 1854 but it is probably the only map to include the Exeter & Yeovil railway line as projected. As the actual South Western line was completed in 1860 the map must have shortly pre-dated the arrival of the new line.

Title: **MAP OF EXETER.**
Size: 185 x 233 mm with *Scale of Feet* 1000 = 40mm (or 1 Mile = 211 mm).
Imprint: *FEATHERSTONE Lithographer 246 HIGH STREET Exeter.* There is a note below this: *CIRCULATING LIBRARY BEDFORD STREET. See below* (all top left in plain panel).

Note the inset plan showing the location of Featherstone's Circulating Library and their printing office (bottom left). There is a scale bar, North point (west is at top) and two tables of Reference – Churches and Chapels. The prison shape has been altered from that in Featherstone's earlier plan, and now has the correct H form. The South Devon Railway is clearly shown and the *Intended Exeter & Yeovil Railway.*

**41.    *John Murray I***                                                                                   *1863*

The late 1830s had seen the introduction of the handbook or guide book and the prominence of the two publishing houses who would dominate the British market for guidebooks throughout the Victorian era: Murray (*Handbook*) and A & C Black (*Guide*). Murray´s first map of Exeter appeared as early as 1863 but it would not be until 1881 that A & C Black included a plan in their guide (49). John Murray (1778-1843) started the famous series of red-bound guides in 1836 but it was his son, also John, who produced the first county guide; *A Handbook for Travellers in Devon & Cornwall* was first published in 1850. The early editions did not include any town maps, but the 5th edition of 1863 included a map of Exeter. In the 9th edition of 1879 the map was replaced by one by Edward Weller (see 48).

Title: **EXETER**
Size: 125 x 100 mm but no scale.
No signature and no imprint.

A fairly simple map of the city extending from St. Thomas to the Cavalry Barracks, showing the new railway and the station off Queen Street. Below the map is a list of 7 buildings. Two notes: *To Veitch's Nursery* (bottom right) and *To face page 17* (below central).

The map appeared again in *A Handbook for Travellers in Devon and Cornwall* sixth and *A Handbook for Travellers in Devonshire* eighth editions. The 6th edition of the handbook was published in 1865: page reference **6**, **Route 1 – Exeter** and **Sect. 1** all added above plan; **To face page 17** deleted (illustrated left). For the eighth edition of 1872 (there was no seventh edition) all added notes were removed along with the reference to Veitch's Nursery and Albert Museum was added to the list of buildings (illustrated right).

**40.**  *Featherstone II 1858*

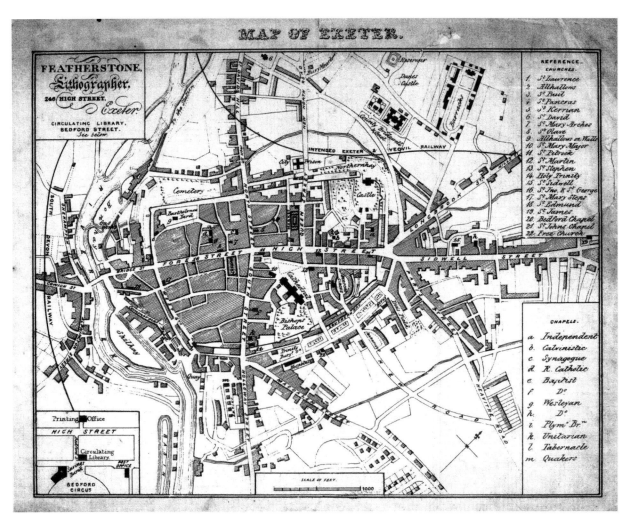

**41.**  *Murray I  1863*

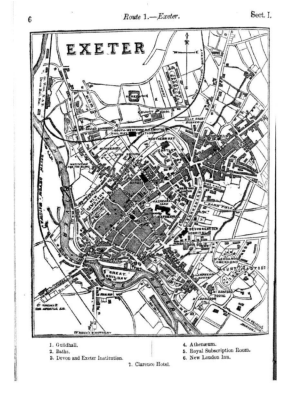

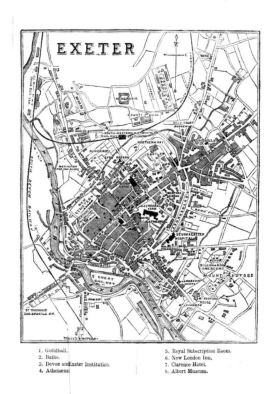

## 42.  *Henry James*                                                                    *1868*

In 1867 the Boundary Commission produced 196 plans of English Boroughs and 51 of Welsh Boroughs. Although the report purported to include each Borough *and County*, very few county or part-county maps were included.[1] Henry James (1803-1877) had overseen the initial stages of the later surveying of towns and boroughs in the West Country. He joined the Ordnance Survey in 1827 and became the Director-General in 1854, a post he held until 1875. James was a supporter of lithography and his enthusiasm for the new technique of photo-zincography led to it becoming a standard process in the production of Ordnance Survey maps. He became a Fellow of the Royal Society, was knighted in 1860 and promoted to Lieutenant-General in 1874.

The boundary maps were prepared under the direction of Captain R M Parsons by lithographic transfer with overprinted colour representing the parliamentary boundary of 1832, the proposed Parliamentary boundary of 1868, the municipal boundary, and the parish and township boundaries see also B&B 146). A note explains that: *A map of each Borough and County taken from the Ordnance Survey plans is appended to the Reports for the purpose of illustrating the existing and proposed Boundaries. These maps, however, many of which are of old date, are far from conveying an adequate idea of the extension of building which has taken place in recent years, and must not be considered as indicating the character of the Districts within the new proposed Boundaries.* The report was printed by George Edward Eyre and William Spottiswoode for HMSO.

Title: **EXETER**
Size: 330 x 220 mm with *Scale of 3 Inches to One Mile* (or 1 Mile = 75 mm).
Signature: *Henry James Colonel Royal Engineers* (in hand).
Imprint: *Zincographed at the Ordnance Survey Office Southampton under the superintendence of Capt. R. M. Parsons R.E., F.R.A.S. Col. Sir H. James R.E., F.R.S. &c. Director* and date below *1868*.

The panel below the map contains James' signature, scale bar and reference for boundary colours. The title is in a panel top right. The plan covers the whole Exeter area from Cowley Bridge to High Wear and from Wick Lane to East Ponford. The only boundary changes proposed from those of 1832 are in the parish of St. Thomas the Apostle north of Foxhays to just below Exwick and straightening the south boundary by Marsh Barton Lane. But the area names have changed and wards have gone. The five outer areas are now St. David, St. Sidwell, St. Leonard, St. Thomas the Apostle and Heavitree.

---

[1] Besides Devonshire only 8 county maps were included: Cheshire, Derby, Essex, (North and South) Lancs, Lincs, Norfolk, Somerset and Staffs. There were further maps of West Kent, East Surrey and the West Riding of Yorkshire.

**42.**                                                          *James 1868*

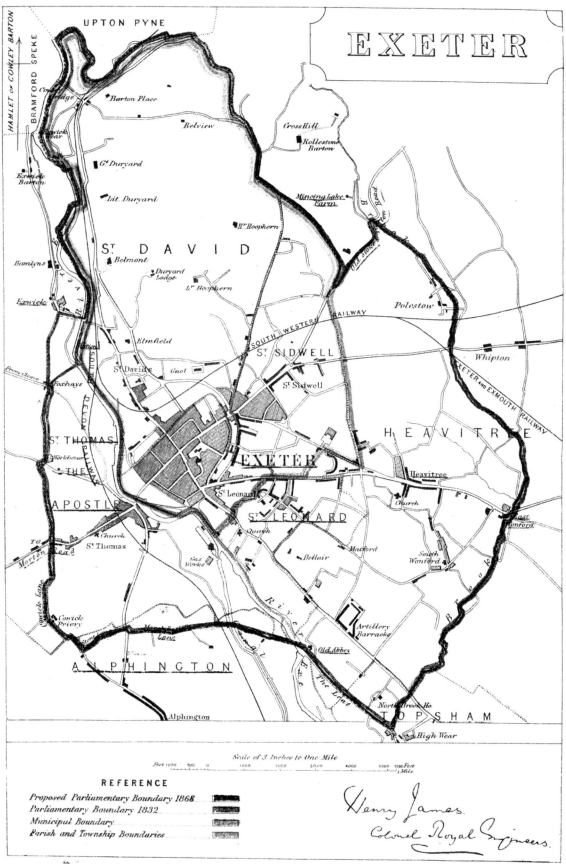

**43.  British Association**                                                    *1869*

The British Association for the Advancement of Science was founded in 1831 on the lines of a German Institution. William Vernon Harcourt and J F W Johnston were leading advocates of the association in competition with the Royal Society. The first meeting was held in York but annual meetings were held in different cities; in 1869 Exeter was chosen.

Although a guide of sorts may have been printed for attendees only a copy of a specially produced map has been seen by the authors and this has been loosely inserted into a copy of Murray's *Handbook for Travellers* (1859)[1]. However it is highly probable that the map was issued to participants as part of a welcome pack or possibly together with the following work which would have been presented or sold to each participant who had attended the British Association meeting held in Exeter: *Report Of The British Association For The Advancement Of Science Held At Exeter In 1869*. This work was published in 1870 by John Murray, London. It was part of an extremely important annual series of original research papers. Containing 800-1000 pp it included 100-120 pp to the rear listing all the members of the association with their qualifications and addresses.

Title: **BRITISH ASSOCIATION  EXETER MEETING 1869**
Size: 134 x180 mm and *SCALE OF YARDS* (600 = 48mm) (or 1 Mile = 140 mm).

This is a simple block plan naming principal streets, the railways and principal buildings with just under half the area taken up with a list of the Section Rooms and references to other map notes, mostly hotels, above the scale bar. Note the new Albert Memorial Museum; the Fairpark on Magdalen Rd; Rougemont (for castle area); the note *Old Cemetery disused*; the two telegraph offices; the inaccuracy of the layout to the reservoirs (north of the county gaol); the cross shaped county prison; the alignment of the castle; and the walls are not shown. The Victoria Public Hall was rushed to completion in time for the meeting and was used for concerts, meetings and lectures until the turn of the century. Illustrated page 18.

**44.  Robert Dymond I**                                                  *1873 (1773)*

Robert Dymond's book, *History of the Suburban Parish of St. Leonard, Exeter* was published in 1873. In it, Dymond included an up to date map of the city and also a similar map to show the changes since 1773. In 1882 he published a similar work on the Parish of St. Petrock.

Title: **ST. LEONARD 1773**
Size: 180 x 209 but no scale.
Imprint: *G. Wolfenden, Lith, Exon*

Shows the area from the Cathedral northeast to Liverydole and southeast to the site of St. James Priory bounded by Magdalen Road and the River Exe.

**45.  Robert Dymond II**                                                       *1873*

Title: **ST. LEONARD 1873**
Size: 180 x 209 mm but no scale.
Imprint: *G. Wolfenden, Lith, Exon*

Shows the area east of the Cathedral as before but James Priory is now Old Abbey. Shows the extensive development in Mount Radford together with Topsham Barracks and the changes to the river (e.g. Trews Wear and Salmon Pool near Old Abbey).

---

[1] At the Exeter Westcountry Studies Library (sWES/1859/HAN).

**44.**                                                        *Dymond I   1873 (1773)*

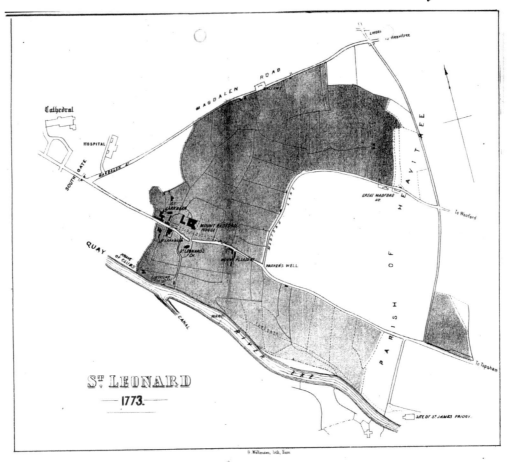

**45.**                                                        *Dymond II  1873*

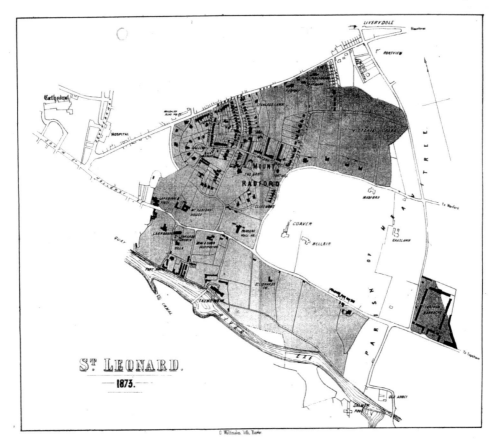

**46.   Thomas Kerslake**                                                                  *1873 (925)*

Thomas Kerslake (1812-1891) was born and educated in Exeter but moved to Bristol in 1827. With his brother-in-law he became a second hand bookseller. Although the partnership was dissolved in 1839 he continued in business and retired in 1870 after a disastrous fire. He then became interested in antiquarian studies, especially the Anglo-Saxon period of the south-west, and wrote a number of articles including one in 1890 about a fictional leader in Saxon southwest, *Saint Richard the King of Englishmen.*

Strictly speaking this is the second printed map of Exeter as it purports to show the area covered by the Saxon mound with the early fortifications at Exeter imposed as it might have been in 925, 1286 and 1778 A.D. It was included in an essay presented by Kerslake to the Archaeological Society. Kerslake wrote about the old division of the City '*The Celt & Teuton in Exeter*' and it was printed in the *Archaeological Journal*, Volume 30 (pp.211-225), 1873. A number of changes were carried out before it appeared in *Saint Richard*; title moved to right; references under map removed; and the shaded area is a little different.

Title: **EXETER. A.D. 925-1286-1778**.
Size:190 x 120 mm within borders with references below. No scale.
Signature: *Standidge & Co. Litho, London E.C.*

A simple outline plan showing the streets and churches within the city walls, with both the old bridge and Stepcote Lane and the current bridge and Fore Street. The key numbers refer to the adjacent text where Kerslake describes a 'double city' with the southern part English and the Northern part British, noting the Celtic saints in the various Chapels north of the High Street.

**47.   George Washington Bacon**                                                          *1876*

Edward Weller could not have imagined how long his maps (county maps, town plans and maps of the railway networks) would continue to be published when he executed them for the *Weekly Despatch* in 1858 (B&B 136). Issued first with that newspaper at regular intervals, they were bound into atlases published by the same company in 1863. Cassell, Petter & Galpin took over the plates and produced a variety of publications with the county maps. George Washington Bacon bought the plates *c.*1868 and from 1869 to the early years of the twentieth century reissued the county maps in atlases, e.g. *New Large Scale Ordnance Atlas of the British Isles*, as well as producing folding maps for the burgeoning leisure industry. Devonshire appeared as two sheets in most of the atlas issues but could be found together or separated in covers as a folding map. In one of these single sheet county map issues, circa 1876, a small inset map of Exeter was introduced.

Title: **EXETER** (written over map area)
Size: 96 mm diameter with *Scale One Mile to the Inch.*

Circular plan of the city included on a folding map of Devon circa 1876 with the cover: *Bacon's New Pocket Map of Devon.* Showing surrounding areas as far as Alphington, Heavitree and St. Thomas. (See also larger illustration on title page.)

**46.**                                                                     *Kerslake 1873 (925)*

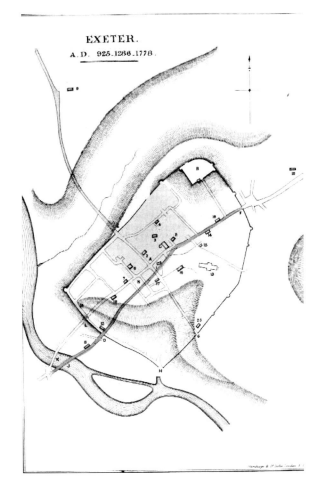

**47.**                                                                     *Bacon 1876*

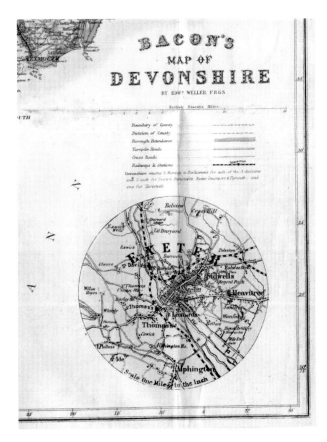

**48.   John Murray II**                                                                                                    *1879*

So popular were John Murray's red-bound books that the company separated Devon & Cornwall in the 9th edition of 1879 and introduced a new, and considerably improved, map for Exeter (replaces 41) for the Devonshire handbook. The plan was used in the Tenth and Eleventh Editions of Murray's *A Handbook for Travellers in Devonshire* until 1901.

Title: **EXETER for Murray's Handbook for Devon**
Size: 160 x 190 mm but no scale.
Signature: *Edwd Weller* (engraver) and publisher's imprint: *London: John Murray Albemarle St.*

The plan covers the area from St. Thomas to Polsloe Park and from the Canal Basin to Exwick. It is the first map to have a grid system to aid finding locations. Although rather a small map it is accurate and detailed and would have been a useful aid to the traveller.
Revised copies of the plan were used in the later 10th edition of 1887 (with only minor amendments – List of 14 buildings and Bridewell (at B3) becomes Governors and Chaplains houses). The 11th edition of 1895 has roads added and named, especially in quadrants A5-6 and E5; a tunnel under the Tiverton Road for S. W. Railway (A7); and the area northwest of the Workhouse and west of Diocesan Trinity College is extensively developed (C-D6).

**49.   A & C Black / Bartholomew**                                                                              *1881*

Adam Black (1784-1874) started the Edinburgh firm in 1807, his nephew Charles not joining the firm until 1833. Their first Scottish guides appeared in 1839 and in 1843 they published their first *Guide to England and Wales*. The first guide to the southwest appeared in 1855 with a new, completely revised edition, appearing in 1862 (Devon with Cornwall and Dorset). However, the Devon text was extracted and used concurrently in *Black's Guide to Devonshire*. From the 12th edition of *Black's Guide to England and Wales* (1881) and the 11th edition of *Black's Guide to Devonshire* (1882) a map of Exeter was included. Apart from the size the two maps were virtually the same. Though only acknowledged in the former work the map was executed by John Bartholomew of Edinburgh.

Title:  **EXETER**
Size: 90 x 140 mm with *Scale of ¼ mile* (20mm) (or 1 Mile = 80 mm).
Signature: *J.Bartholomew, Edinr.* and imprint *A. & C. Black, Edinburgh.*

A simple street plan from St. Thomas to Polsloe Park and St. David's Station to *Deaf and Dumb Inst.* Churches, main roads and principal buildings are noted. Published in 1881 in *Black's Guide to England and Wales* (12th edition) as described.
In 1882 the map appeared for the first time in a county guide, *Black's Guide to Devonshire* (11th edition, see illustration). The title remained the same but the map was reduced to 90 x 80 mm and signature removed. A topographical note below shows Hotels; Railway Stations; the Distance from London; the Post Office, Population of Municipal Borough (1881) 37,608, Returns 2 M.P's (sic).
The map remained unchanged in the subsequent county editions: 12th (1884), and 13th (1889) but the information below the map changed. In the 14th edition of *Black□s Guide to Devonshire Castle St Ch* is rewritten to give space for the *New Theatre*, the Post Office has moved from Queen Street to High Street, the *Cemetery* has lost the word *New*. The Topographical Guide includes *Poples New London* hotel, and the *Bude, White Lion* and the *City Commercial* hotels and the population figure is altered (1891) 37,580.

**48.**                                                                    *Murray II 1879*

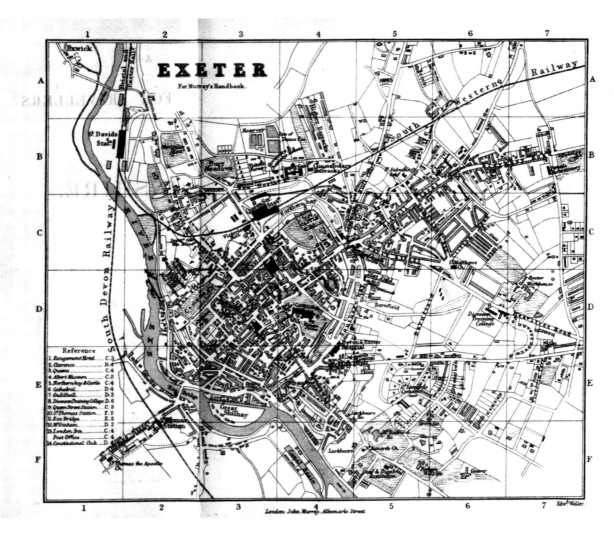

**49.**                                                              *Black / Bartholomew 1881*

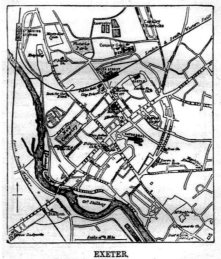

**EXETER.**

Hotels: *Rougemont*, Queen Street, opposite South-Western Station; *Pople's New London*, off High Street; *Royal Clarence*, and *The Globe*, Cathedral Yard; *Queen's*, Queen Street; *Half Moon*, High Street. There are also two small but handy hotels, *The Railway* and *The Elmfield*, close to St. David's Station.

Railway Stations: London and South-Western, Queen Street, near centre of city. St. David's, Great-Western and L. and S.-W., half a mile away. St. Thomas's (G.-W. only) on the South Devon portion of the line, in the S.W. part of the city.

Distance from London by L. and S.-W. 172 m. ; time, 4h. By G.-W. 194 m. ; time, 4h. 15m.

Post-Office (Queen Street).

Population of Municipal Borough, (1881) 37,665. Returns 2 M.P's.

### 50.  *Cassell & Co. Ltd I*                                                                                             *1882*

*Our Own Country ... Descriptive, Historical, Pictorial* was produced originally in 1882 (two volumes in a five-volume set are dated) and sometime later also for subscribers in 6 volumes. There were five maps in total covering Devon, each set in a page of text in the various volumes. The maps are: Map of the Course of the Plym, Map of North Devon, Map of South Devon, Old Plan of Exeter (a small copy of Braun & Hogenberg) and Map of Exeter. Although the volumes are packed with maps and plans, many have no scale and only maps in the fifth volume of the early set had a printer's signature. All maps are very small with little detail.

Cassells also published J R Chanter's *Lundy Island* complete with a map of the island possibly executed by Chanter himself and a further map of Exeter was published in their guide to the L&SWR in 1888 (57).

Title: **MAP OF EXETER.**
Size: 85 x 134 mm with no scale, no signature or imprint.

The area covered is from Hermitage to Heavitree and only shows the roads and the railways. This appears in Volume 2, p.161 of *Our Own Country ... Descriptive, Historical, Pictorial* published in London, Paris & Melbourne by Cassell & Co., Ltd in 1882 with reissues in 1898.

### 51.  *Alfred Vincent*                                                                                                 *1884*

The following map can be found in a guide published by Alfred Vincent, a local printer and publisher: *Vincent's Guide to Exeter*. Alfred Vincent published this guide in 1884 but by 1889 Mrs Alfred Vincent was carrying on the business as lithographic printer at 1 Maddocks Row and was still in business at the same address in 1893.

Title: **GROUND PLAN OF EXETER**
Size: 192 x 252 mm but no scale.
Imprint: *A. Vincent, Exeter Lith.*

This is a simplified street plan showing prominent buildings (some of which are drawn in elevation, e.g. St. Michael's Ch.). The drawing is rough, inaccurate and sometimes misleading even though it shows nearly all the important buildings. It is interesting to note that some place names are upside down, the Catholic Cathedral at Palace Gate, the Ferry at Quay Lane, the incorrect railway siding in to the Basin and the complete absence of the city walls. The map is the last to show the theatre in Bedford Street as this was ravaged by fire in February 1885 and was replaced by a new building in Longbrook Street.

**50.** *Cassell & Co. Ltd I  1882*

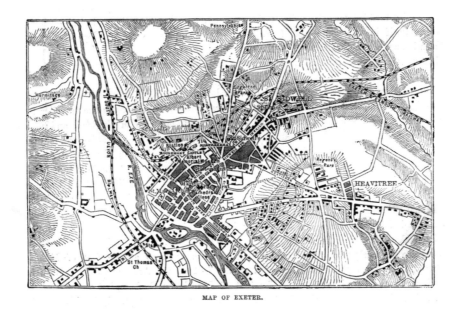

MAP OF EXETER.

**51.** *Vincent 1884*

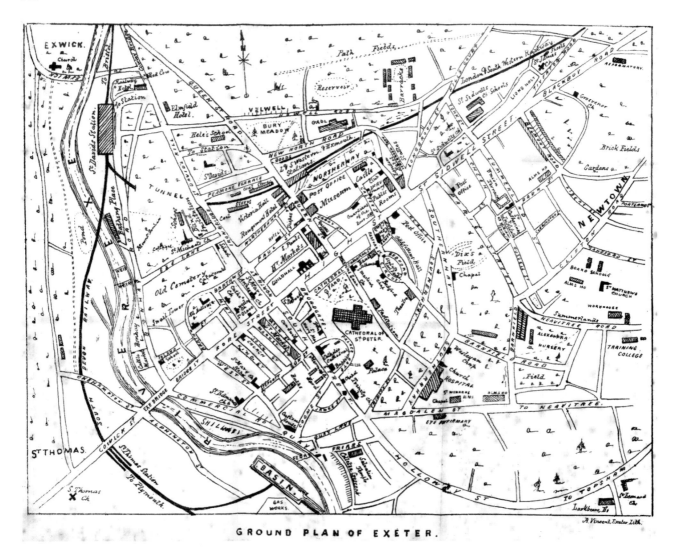

GROUND PLAN OF EXETER.

**52. *Dulau / Bartholomew*** **1884**

The Dulau company began their famous *Thorough Guide Series* in 1882 (North Devon and Cornwall) and 1884 (South Devon and Cornwall). The editors (and probably authors) were M J B Baddeley and Charles Slegg Ward, hence the series became known as the Baddeley & Ward series.

Mountford John Byrde Baddeley (1843-1906), a school master, earned his reputation as the compiler of these *Thorough Guide books for pedestrians*. He settled in the Lake District which he popularized as a pleasure resort. According to the advertising text in the guides: *In English topographical writing for tourists, the Thorough Guide Series is so far ahead of any other that there can scarcely be said to be a good second to it.* (*Saturday Review*, August 28th, 1886). *The Times* (August 3rd, 1887) even went so far as to compare a *Baddeley* with a *Baedeker*. A cursory glance at the contents page and page numbering of different editions seems to imply little up-dating, however, a lot of new detail was added for each issue.

In the two volumes, a total of 28 maps of Devon and Cornwall areas were included. The Exeter map was included in both the South and the North guides from 1884.

Title: **EXETER**
Size: 150 x 205 mm with *Scale of 1/4 Mile* (40 mm).
Signature: *J Bartholomew Edinr.*

Initially the map has a scale, and even has a reference to *Tramway Routes*[1], but the plan has no shading and no graticule (see top illustration, South edition 1884). It only shows the main roads and the principal buildings. The map appeared in all the following:

*Thorough Guide ... North Devon And North Cornwall Second Edition, Revised* (1884)
*Thorough Guide ... North Devon And North Cornwall Third Edition, Revised* (1885-1886)
*Thorough Guide ... North Devon And North Cornwall Fourth Edition, Revised* (1888)
*Thorough Guide ... North Devon And North Cornwall Fifth Edition, Revised* (1891-92)
*Thorough Guide ... North Devon And North Cornwall Sixth Edition, Revised.* (1892-1894)
*Thorough Guide ... North Devon And North Cornwall Seventh Edition, Revised.* (1896-1901)

*Thorough Guide Series: No. VII ... South Devon And South Cornwall. First Edition* (1884)
*Thorough Guide ... South Devon And South Cornwall Second Edition, Revised (1885-1887)*
*Thorough Guide ... South Devon And South Cornwall Third Edition Revised.* (1889-1890)
*Thorough Guide ... South Devon And South Cornwall Fourth Edition, Revised.* (1891-1892)
*Thorough Guide ... South Devon And South Cornwall Fifth Edition, Revised.* (1895-1901)

The only major changes were carried out prior to the 1890 South Devon issue. A list of Railway Stations and Hotels has been added outside the map area (left). The Key now has City Walls. A graticule (grid system) has been laid over the map and there are numerous new inclusions, e.g. Barnfield Road and Barnfield Crescent. Some building names have changed, e.g. Bude Haven Hotel (now Bude Hotel), Cavalry Barracks is Higher Barracks and Free Ch (now Wesleyan Chapel) etc. The original theatre has now become the Drill Hall (the old theatre in Bedford Street) and there is a New Theatre in Longbrook Street, the foundation stone was laid in May and the theatre opened in October 1886.

For some 1892/1893 and 1901 issues the List of Railway Stations and Hotels has been moved inside the map area (see illustration below right, 1890 North edition).

---

[1] The first horse-drawn tram route was opened between St. Sidwell and Heavitree in 1882.

**52.**                                                        *Dulau / Bartholomew   1884*

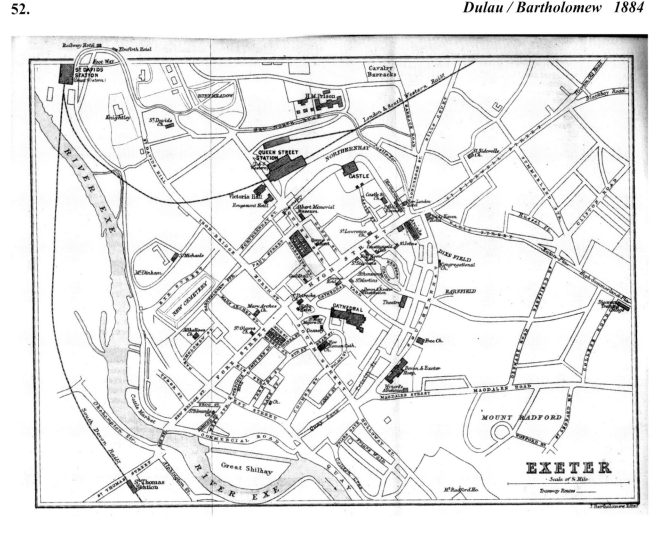

*Dulau / Bartholomew   1890*

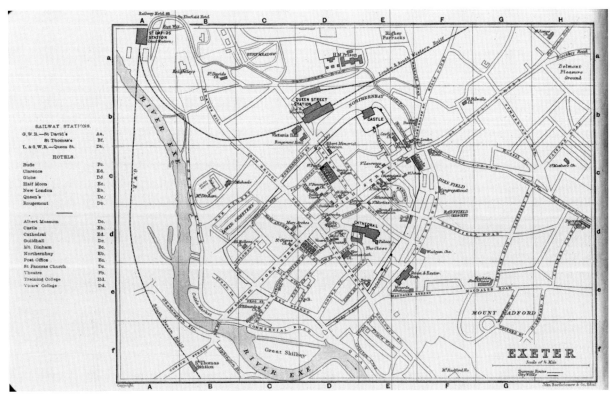

## 53.   Freeman I                                                                          *1887*

Edward Augustus Freeman (1823-1892) was a medieval and constitutional historian famous for his *History of the Norman Conquest*. In 1887 the history of Exeter appeared as one of the *Historic Towns* series edited by Freeman and the Rev. William Hunt and which actually included a total of four maps. Besides the two maps included below, Freeman's work contained small reproductions of both Braun and Hogenberg (3) and a copy of Daniel Lysons' representation of the very early manuscript map of Henry VIII (see Lysons, 19). An Edward A Freeman wrote a long section on architecture for inclusion in *Baedeker's Guides to Great Britain* (this did not include a map of Exeter until the 1900s).
Both of these maps were printed in Freeman□s *History of Exeter: Historic Towns – Exeter by Edward A Freeman, DCL, LL D.* which was published by Longmans, Green and & Co., of London, New York and Bombay in 1887 with a *Second Edition* of 1890 and a *Third Edition* in 1892 and 1901.

Title: **EXETER 1886**
Size: 245 x 160 mm with *Scale of Feet* (800 = 41 mm) (or 1 Mile = 270 mm).
Imprint: *Longmans, Green, & Co., London, New York, and Bombay.*

A simple street plan covering only the central area from the bridge to St. Sidwell's and from Queen Street Station to the Devon & Exeter Hospital. Built up areas are shaded. The city wall is shown with the old gates named and the line of the old bridge pecked. Note the reference within the castle grounds that they belong to the County of Devon and also a dashed line off the High Street and crossing South Street with a note *Site of Ikenild Way*.[1]

## 54.   Freeman II                                                                         *1887*

Title: **EXETER in the ELEVENTH CENTURY**.
Size: 135 x 85 mm with *Scale* (1/2 mile = 35 mm).
Signature: *Stanford's Geogl Estabt* and imprint:
*London: Longmans & Co.*

Simply hachured map showing the main roads and walls. This is very similar to the plan included by Kerslake (46) and is found in *Historic Towns – Exeter by Edward A Freeman* (see above for details).

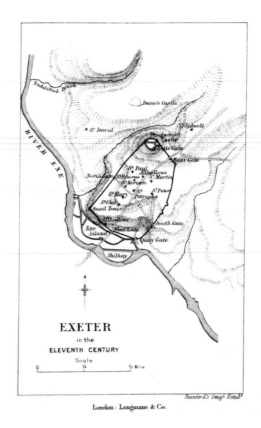

---

[1] This is possibly the route of a Roman Road, but the Icknield Way runs from Ivinghoe Beacon in Buckinghamshire to Knettishall Heath in Norfolk and claims to be the oldest road in Britain.

**53.**                                                    *Freeman I 1887*

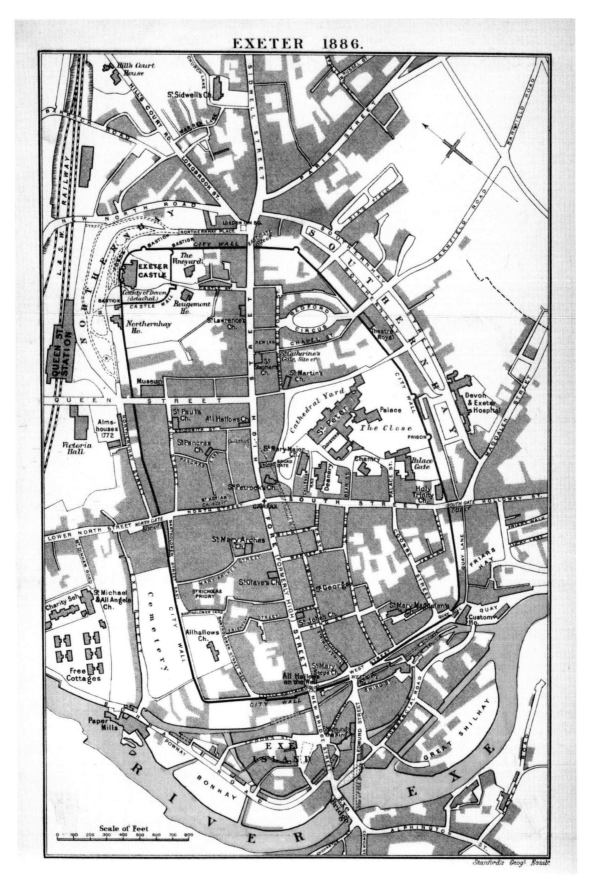

EXETER 1886.

## 55.   *Ward & Lock I*                                                 *1887*

Ebenezer Ward and George Lock started their own firm on Midsummer's Day, 1854. The Locks were an influential Dorchester family and George Lock's father had married Eliza Galpin making George Lock (1832-1891) first cousin to Thomas Dixon Galpin, later to make his name with Cassell, Petter and Galpin. Ebenezer Ward (1819-1902) was a manager for the *Illustrated London News* publishers' book business. The two were introduced by Thomas Galpin and Ward & Lock was launched with a £1000 loan from George Lock senior, the articles of partnership being signed June 23rd, 1854. After initial friendly relations and support, contact between the two cousins was broken when Galpin and his partner, George William Petter, took over Cassell's to found a rival business partnership. From 1891 until *c.*1897 James Bowden was a partner and they traded as Ward, Lock and Bowden Ltd.[1]

Ward and Lock guides often included maps first published by Henry Besley in the 1850s and smaller maps (e.g. Exeter or Lynmouth) printed by G Philip and Son. Ward & Lock published a number of titles covering Devon; Bideford (from approx. 1897); Dartmoor (1895); Dawlish (1898); Exeter (1898); Exmouth (1898); Ilfracombe (1896); Lynton and Lynmouth (1886); Plymouth (1895); Sidmouth (1899); Teignmouth (1898); and Torquay (1884).[2] The Exeter plan appeared in *Ward & Lock's Pictorial and Historical Guide To North Devon* (circa 1887) and *Ward & Lock's Pictorial and Historical Guide To South Devon* (circa 1888).

### Title: **EXETER**
Size: 186 x 263 mm with *Scale of ¼ Mile*  (50 mm).
Imprint:  *G. Philip & Son, Fleet Street.*

This is a simple street plan, limited to main roads, with principal buildings blocked and named. The area covered is from St. Thomas Station to St. David's Station and southeast to the Training College.

## 56.   *Ordnance Survey*                                               *1888*

In 1888 the Ordnance Survey produced an *Index to the Ordnance Survey of Devonshire Shewing Civil Parishes*. It was reissued the same year as the *Diagram of the Sanitary Districts in Devonshire* and again in 1891 with the first title (B&B 164). These maps included an inset map of Exeter (illustrated is inset plan only). In the same year the Ordnance Survey published the results of their now revised survey of Exeter made in 1875-6. This was published in 41 sheets, each sheet covering an area 0.2 by 0.3 miles at a scale of 1:500 and numbered as sub-divisions of their 1:2500 sheets. These were revised in 1890. In 1890 Exeter's plans drawn at 1:10,560 (the 6" to the mile) were published on 4 sheets (80 NW, NE, SW, SE). They were revised in 1906 in 1932 and again in 1938.

At the same time, 1887-1892 Charles E Goad produced *Insurance Plans for Exeter,* at a scale of 1in to 40ft (1:480). These plans were leased and not sold and were continually updated by paste-on slips until 1962. In 1968 they were replaced by their *Shopping Centre Plans* which are updated at least every two years. The current scale is 1:1000.

### Title: **Enlarged Sketch of Portion of the City & County of the City of Exeter.**
Size of inset: 115 x 115 mm but no scale.

The plan shows the parishes with a reference key (bottom right). Note the two areas within the City boundary that are still part of Devon County: A is the County Gaol and B is the Castle. Heavitree, St. Leonard and St. Thomas the Apostle are shown outside the city/county boundary (the old municipal boundary).

---

[1] Edward Liveing; *Adventure in Publishing – The House of Ward Lock 1854-1954*; Ward, Lock & Co. Ltd; 1954.

[2] Based on information at www.wardlockredguides.co.uk, British Library and EWSL holdings and author's own collection.

**55.**                                                              *Ward & Lock I 1887*

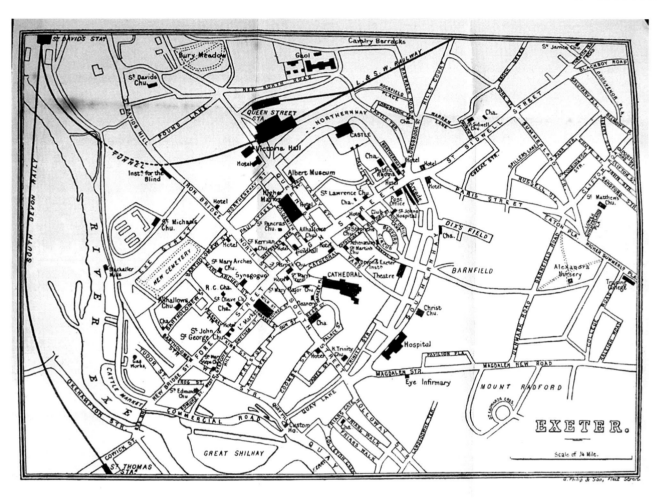

**56.**                                                              *Ordnance Survey 1888*

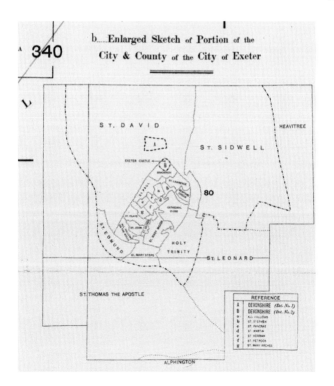

## 57.   *Cassell & Co. Ltd  II*                                                      *1888*

Amongst many railway publications and timetables published by the various operators a few were issued with maps. From 1888 Cassell & Co. published *The Official Guide to the London & South Western Railway*. This guide contained a number of maps (including a county map of Devon; B&B 165) and plans of railway stations, including Exeter and Plymouth.

Title: **PLAN OF EXETER**
Size: 130 x 200 mm. No Scale. Printed in light red.
Imprints: *London and South Western Railway Official Guide* and *Cassell & Company, Limited, London*.

The plan can be found in *The Official Guide to the London & South Western Railway* published in London by Cassell & Co., Ltd. First issued in 1888 it was most probably published annually but only reissues of 1889 and 1891 known.

## 58.   *Kelly / Bryer*                                                              *1889*

In 1799 Frederick Festus Kelly, His Majesty's Inspector of Inland Letter carriers, created the Post Office London Directory. In 1802 Kelly & Co. was launched and c.1845 began the production of county directories. Devon first appeared in 1856 with a county map executed by the Becker company (B&B 132). This was reissued at c.5-yearly intervals with updated maps. The last issue of the directory seen with Becker's map is that of 1873. For the next issue of 1883 a new map was engraved and lithographed by F Bryer (B&B 159). When this was reissued in 1889 inset plans of Exeter and Plymouth had been added to the map. Illustrated is the inset plan from the 1889 issue.

Title: **PLAN OF EXETER** – inset to Kelly's Map of Devon (top right)
Size: 107 x 123 mm with *Scale 2 Inches to 1 Mile* (= 50 mm).
Imprint below complete map: *London: Kelly's Directory Office, 51 Gt. Queen Street*.

The simple plan covers an area from Exwick (top left) to Wonford (bottom right) with only main roads and the rail lines being shown.
Kelly reissued his directories at roughly four year intervals. The words *To Exmouth* were added to that railway line for the 1893 issue. There was no further change in the later issues (1897 and 1900).

**57.**                                                    *Cassell & Co. Ltd II 1888*

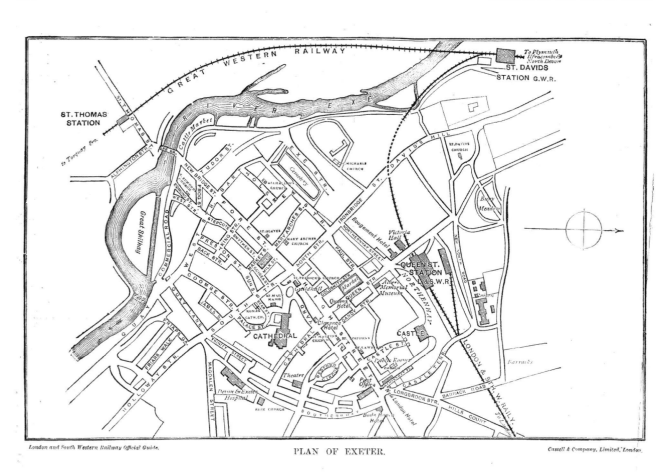

**58.**                                                    *Kelly / Bryer 1889*

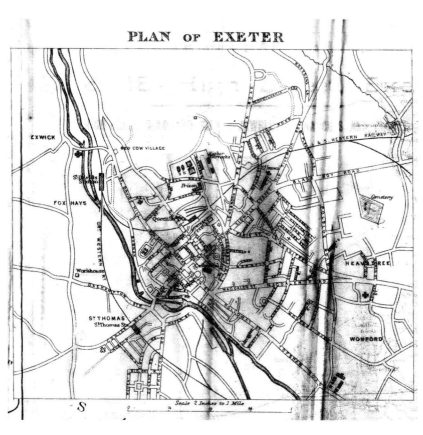

**59.   *John Hooker / Reynolds I***                                                   *1892*

Herbert Edward Reynolds, a local historian and author of a short history of the diocese, edited a number of items from the Cathedral Archives including some plans and writings by John Hooker and brought them to the attention of a wider public in his *An Original Manuscript Of John Hooker, Chamberlain Of The City Of Exeter 1555*. This was published in 1892 and included illustrations of two of John Hooker's manuscript plans made 300 years earlier.[1] Reynolds' book included a Preface from Hooker's '*Great History of Exeter*' – *now in the Guild Hall of the same City Written by his own hand, and never before printed* – and included descriptive notes and an introduction. Hence, although John Hooker's original manuscript plan was executed in 1590 it was not until 1892 that the plan of St. Sidwell's (below) or the Churchyard (next entry) were first printed.

Though there is no actual title to the plan described below there is text written within a rectangle which describes the limits of the Fee '*And so forth by the middle of ye same waye to a lile water there called Shyttebrooke, And downe by ye midle of the same brooke unto ye Southe ende & corner of a garden of ye sayde Prior of St. Johns adioynante yto the same brooke wch garden lyeth in the West Syde of the same brooke and within the soyle Fee & ground afore sayde. And so from ye same South ende & corner by and by dytch of ye same garden into a pathe westewardes lyinge betwene ye landes called St Johns feeldes on ye one partie, and ye Soyle Fee & ground aforesayde on the other partie. And so forthe in the same pathe westewardes unto a close of William menardes. And so by ye midle of ye same close over the close sometimes of Roger Golde in y southe partie and ye barne of ye sayde Thomas Bernes ats Renolde in ye north partye And so out into the high waye called Croldich waye, And so forth by ye midle of ye same waye Northwards betwene ye garden and tenement of John at Forde in the west parte into ye high waye cominge from Exeter to St Annes Chappell &c.*'

Title: No title but shows the area of St. Sidwell's Fee
Size: 260 x 285 mm. A compass (top) but no scale.

The plan shows the Fee of St. Sidwell, part of the castle and the city walls from the east gate round to the south gate. Features of note include the Guildhall[2] at the corner of Paris Street; the doorway through the wall into the close; the Alms houses; three county stones; and St. Karlet's Cross.

In 1911 William Pollard published *An Account of the sieges of Exeter by John Hoker – transcribed by William J Harte*. This work contained other plans executed by Hooker usually with his imprint: *William Pollard & Co. Ltd. Lithographers, Exeter & London*.

**60.   *John Hooker / Reynolds II***                                                  *1892*

The second plate included in Reynolds' work. For source, see last entry.

Title: No title but sketch plan of the **Churchyard**
Size: 228 x 290 mm but there is no scale.

The second plan is a drawing looking south east showing the precinct and the north east corner of the city. At the top are four coats of arms: The City, The Royal Arms, the eagle of the first Earl Redvers or Rivers and the Bishop's crossed keys. Hooker's own arms are at the bottom.

---

[1] The original drawing and that of the churchyard are part of the collection of Hooker manuscripts formerly held by the Dean and Chapter as D&C.Ex.3530 f.37 and D&C 3530 f.59-60. They are now lodged at the Devon Record Office. Both maps are listed in a Table of Contents to Hooker's history (ECA Book 52) but the maps have no titles: *Platt of St Sidwells Fee*; and *A Platte of the Churchyarde*.

[2] The courts of the Lords of the Fee were held in this guildhall.

**59.**                                                    *Hooker / Reynolds I  1892*

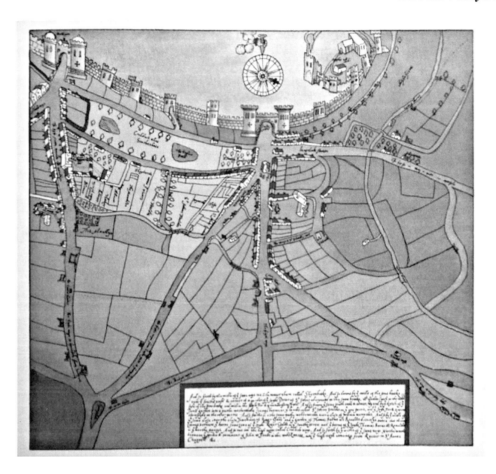

**60.**                                                    *Hooker / Reynolds II  1892*

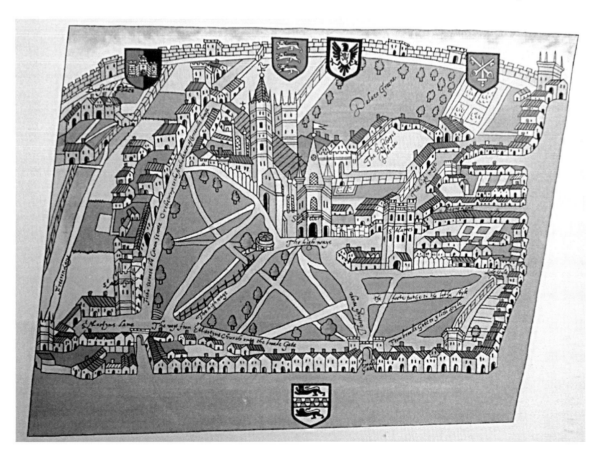

### 61.  **Pollard – Church Congress**                                  *1894*

Thomas Pollard is believed to have first started business as a printer in Exeter in 1791.  Details are sparse, but he was probably using letterpress to print stationery, account books, and advertising pamphlets. In the early 1800s William Carss Pollard is known to have continued the family's printing trade from a factory in 39/40 North Street, Exeter and like most printers at the start of the Victorian era provided whatever their clients requested – from advertising posters to timetables and letterbooks. During the Victorian era and into the early 20th century the business grew substantially under the leadership of William Pollard (son of William Carss) and then his son, Herbert Pollard. They outgrew the premises on North Street and in 1919 opened an impressive new factory at Bampfylde Street. The depression of the 1930s was very tough and during the Second World War trading virtually ceased. On the 4th of May 1942 the factory was completely destroyed in the Exeter Blitz. The company's insurers would not fully cover the claim and after the war the company had to be rebuilt largely from scratch and the company was gradually rebuilt through the 1950s and 60s. When the country's largest manufacturers of weighbridges, Avery and Weightron, were frustrated with the quality of tickets supplied for their machines the Pollard company created a specialised production centre to focus on this market and are the undisputed market leader of weighbridge tickets today.[1]

Although the cover title to the work below is *Pollard's Official History and Guide to Exeter* it is clear from both the map itself and the paragraph of comments on the reverse of the map that this booklet was produced for the visit of the Church Congress which took place in October 1894.

Title: **Church Congress, 1894. KEY MAP OF THE City and County of the City of Exeter.**
Size: 170 x 213 mm but with no scale.
No signature or imprint.

The plan has a type-script panel to the right (forming the third of three folding leaves) which refers to the numbers on the plan, and the use of certain buildings for the Congress. A simple plan of Exeter, only of interest for the congress, with the old city wall line marked red with note to that effect below the map; *The RED line indicates the boundary of the Old City Walls.* The right panel on reverse has information for those attending the congress on rail tickets.

### 62.  **Walker & Boutall**                                          *1895*

In 1895 the Black's fully revised their 15th edition of the Devon Guide (see also 48). It was edited by A R Hope Moncrief and included a new and clearer plan of the City although still covering the same area. Published in *Black's Guide to Devonshire* from the 15th edition.

Title: **PLAN OF EXETER**
Size: 95 x 82 mm with *Scale 1/8 Mile* (¼ = 20 mm, or 1 Mile = 80 mm).
Imprint: *Walker & Boutall sc.*

It is a simple and precise street plan with only main streets named, a North point, a scale bar and 12 numbered references below the map. The railways have the distinctive railway pattern with both the Great Western Railway and the London & South Western Railway with the tunnel by Queen Street Station, and the branch line to the Basin. The key has reference to the Electricity Works (14), i.e. the Rockfield Works in New North Road, built in 1889. The guide was reissued from 1898 with 24 references below the map (and added numbers in map) and with the Public Hall now Victoria Hall.

---

[1] Taken from the Pollard website at: http://pollardsprint.co.uk/history.html.

**61.**                                                                                   *Pollard 1894*

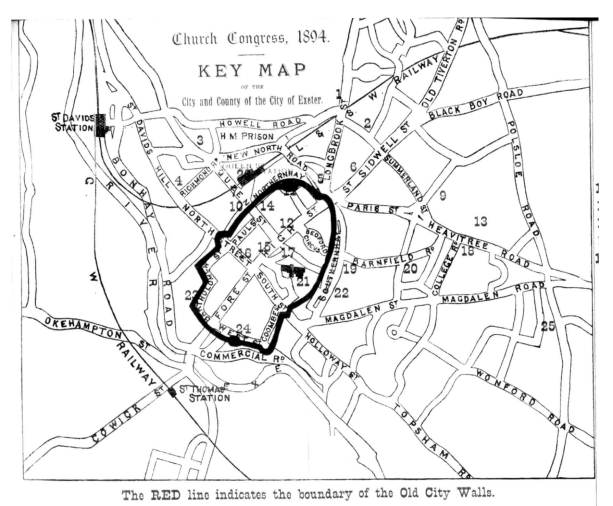

The **RED** line indicates the boundary of the Old City Walls.

**62.**                                                                          *Walker & Boutall  1895*

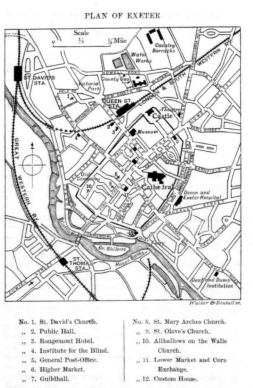

### 63.   *Ward & Lock II*                                                   *1898*

Ward and Lock's original plan of Exeter (see 55 above) was obviously inadequate and in 1898 a new plan, drawn and engraved by George Philip and Son was included when Ward and Lock published their first guide dedicated to Exeter. This plan first appeared in *A Pictorial and Descriptive Guide To Exeter* published in London, New York, and Melbourne by Ward, Lock and Co., Ltd. There was a *Second Edition* in 1900.

Title: **PLAN OF EXETER** above map centrally.
Size: 140 x 190 mm with a *Scale of 1/4 Mile* (1/4 = 31 mm).
Imprint: *WARD, LOCK & Co LTD, WARWICK HOUSE, SALISBURY SQ, LONDON*
Signature: *George Philip & Son, London & Liverpool.*

A simple map of the city centre from St. David's Station and St. Thomas to the workhouse in the east. Only important and public buildings shown and no residential development. The new theatre at the junction of Longbrook Street and New North Road is shown (opened October 1886) and the Electricity Station built in 1889.

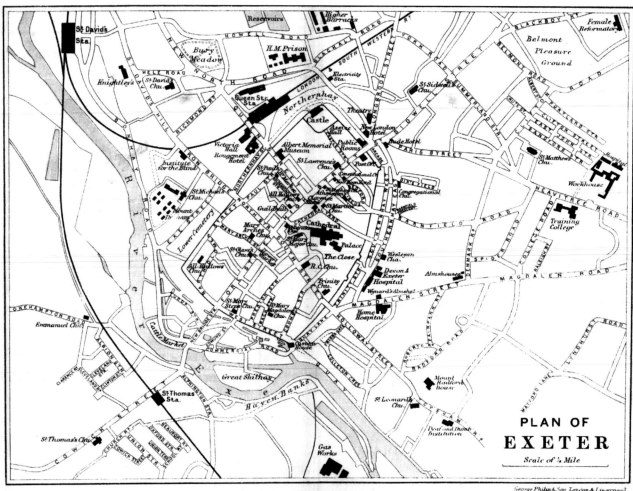

## Select Bibliography

### Books on Devon Maps

Devonshire is probably the English county which has been the most intensely examined in terms of its mapping history. Margery Rowe and Mary Ravenhill have done an enormous amount of work on the manuscript maps and have catalogued, and continue to catalogue, the wealth of manuscript material which has been discovered and which continues to turn up. Roger Kain has provided an atlas of tithe mapping. Elisabeth Stewart published a concise work on Plymouth maps and charts, both manuscript and printed. As far as printed material on county maps is concerned the *Printed Maps of Devonshire 1575 – 1837* appeared in 1996 and the continuation, *The Victorian Maps of Devon 1838 – 1901,* was published in 2000 by Francis Bennett and Kit Batten. In addition Francis Bennett has privately published two books on road maps, both of which go into some detail on Devon history of road mapping.

| | | | |
|---|---|---|---|
| Batten, K and Bennett, F | *The Printed Maps of Devon* | Devon Books | 1996 |
| Batten, K and Bennett, F | *The Victorian Maps of Devon* | Devon Books | 2000 |
| Batten, Kit | *Christopher Saxton and his Map of Devonshire*[1] | | 1990 |
| Batten, Kit | *John Cooke* | Private Printing[2] | 2009 |
| Bennett, Francis | *The Road-Books, Road-Maps of Great Britain 1535-1850* | | |
| | | Privately Printed and Published | 2007 |
| Bennett, Francis | *The Roads of Devon & Cornwall* | Private Printing | 2007 |
| Gray, Todd (Ed.) | *Devon Documents* | (D&C) Notes & Queries | 1996 |
| Gray, Todd (Ed.) | *Tudor and Stuart Devon* | Univ. of Exeter Press | 1992 |
| Harley and O'Donoghue | *The Old Series Ordnance Survey* | Harry Margery | 1977 |
| Kain, Roger | *Tithe maps of England and Wales* | Cambridge Univ. Press | 1995 |
| Ravenhill, W L D | *A Map of the County of Devon* | Devon & Cornwall Record Society | 1965 |
| Ravenhill, M and Rowe, M | *Early Devon Maps* | Friends of Devon''s Archives | 2000 |
| Ravenhill, M and Rowe, M | *Maps of Georgian Devon* | Friends of Devon's Archives | 2002 |
| Ravenhill, M and Rowe, M | *Devon Maps and Map-Makers* | Friends of Devon's Archives | 2002 |
| Stewart, Elisabeth | *Lost Landscapes of Plymouth* | Alan Sutton | 1991 |

### Books on Exeter

| | | | |
|---|---|---|---|
| Brice, Thomas | *The History and Description ...* | Brice | 1802 |
| Gray, Todd | *Lost Exeter: Five Centuries of Change* | Mint Press | 2002 |
| Isaacke, Richard | *Remarkable Antiquities of the City of Exeter* | | 1681 |
| Hoskins, W. G. | *2000 Years in Exeter* | James Townsend & Sons | 1960 |
| Lethbridge, Tony | *Exeter – history and guide* | Tempus Publishing | 2005 |
| Mitchell, John | *Megalithomani* | Thames & Hudson | 1984 |
| Minchinton, W | *Life to the City* | Devon Books | 1987 |
| Passmore, Dick | *The Story of the Theatre Royal* | The Mint Press | 2002 |
| Passmore, Dick | *Power to the City* | Little Silver Publications | 2008 |
| Portman, D | *Exeter Houses 1400-1700* | Univ. of Exeter Press | 1966 |
| Stoyle, Mark | *Exeter's City Walls* | Univ. of Exeter Press | 2003 |
| Youings, Joyce | *Tuckers Hall, Exeter* | Univ. of Exeter Press | 1968 |

Devon County Council maintain a superb internet site with many wonderful articles produced by the Exeter Westcountry Studies Library. Go to their site at www.devon.gov.uk/localstudies and click *Devon Maps* on the *Find Out More* section. The Exeter Working Papers covering all aspects of the book and print trade. For the index to go to http://bookhistory.blogspot.com/2005/12/index.html. There is also a very good site devoted to Exeter, produced and maintained by David Cornforth at www.exetermemories.co.uk.

---

[1] Privately produced monograph comparing the county maps of Devon by Christopher Saxton, John Speed, Jan Jansson and Joan Blaeu. A copy is held at Exeter Westcountry Studies Library.

[2] Privately produced monograph presenting the life and works of John Cooke. A copy is held at Exeter Westcountry Studies Library.

**Appendix A**

**John Hooker – States and Derivatives**

John Hooker's plan went through various stages of development and two further states[1] of the map are known and a number of copies were made. The first state is described on page 22 and is held at the British Library (BL Maps C.5.a.3).
The two later states are;

State 2. The dividers and the scale bar are partly erased, a tree is omitted west of the bridge and *Powe Lane* is changed to *Pound Lane.* Only one copy is known, in the possession of the Dymond family of Chagford.

State 3. A crude, wrongly orientated, compass rose is drawn over the space previously occupied by the dividers. Holloway Road has been incorrectly altered, turning east after Lark Beare and so wrongly moving Malford and the chapel of St. Leonard. Only one copy is known. This state is illustrated on page 23 and also (with state 1) in Todd Gray, 1992; the map is at Devon Record Office (4292A/BS1), part of the Exeter Guildhall Collection.

In c.1593 a four-fold screen was made in gilded leather which portrayed an enlarged copy of the map (1300 x 1640 mm) in a decorated border. Ravenhill and Rowe wrote an explanatory essay[2] which suggested that the screen was made for, or given to, one of the Cecil family, either to Sir William, Lord Burghley, or his son Robert. The screen map is more correct in many details but none more so than the cathedral where the towers are more correctly placed and the windows detailed. The covered walkway in front of the Guildhall is not shown, but nor is the renaissance colonnade, completed in 1594, leading to the suggested date of 1593.
The map was copied by John Speed, Braun & Hogenberg, Daniel Meisner, Matthäus Merian, Rugerus Hermannides and by Richard Izacke's unknown engraver, each adding his own style to the map (see entries 2-7) before Ichabod Fairlove's completely new map became the new standard from which to copy.

Braun and Hogenberg derivatives can be seen by the inclusion of people and sometimes the original title or variation thereof (*Civitas Exoniae*). Various copies were made, the earliest being possibly that executed by Mutlow for Lysons *Magna Britannia* (see entry 19). Townsend (who did a lot of work for Besley) lithographed a copy for inclusion in W Cotton's *An Elizabethan Guild of the City of Exeter*, published 1873; a small version was included in Cassell's *Our Own Country* (50) in 1882; J G Commin, a local publisher, issued *Exeter in circa AD 1570* (a reference to Hooker) but with subheading *From Braun's Civitates Orbis Terrarum* from his premises in the High Street in 1886; Freeman included a small plan in 1887 in his *History of Exeter* (see 53); and another copy, probably by Commins, was printed c.1895 with title *Exeter in 1618* (a clear reference to Hogenberg) with advertisements on the reverse. Interestingly, Commins included the arms of John Hooker on his copies (not included by Braun & Hogenberg).

---

[1] A state is meant to mean that the original plate on which the map was engraved was changed in some way and then used for a new printing run; a copy is a new engraving on a fresh plate.
[2] See William Ravenhill and Margery Rowe; *A Decorated Screen Map of Exeter* based on John Hooker's Map of 1587 in Todd Gray, 1992. The screen is illustrated in full colour.

## Appendix B

## John Richards

John Richards (1690-1788) was born at Mariansleigh, North Devon and received a grammar school education. He was apprenticed to Abraham Voysey, a joiner in St. Thomas's who made Sea-quadrants. He succeeded to a business as joiner and builder and it was as a builder that he designed and built the New Hospital. However, even before completing the hospital he had worked as a surveyor. Although he was carrying out surveys for the Chamber as early as 1739 it was not until September 1746 that he was officially appointed as the City's Surveyor. In 1744, on behalf of the Hospital of St. John, he surveyed the Manors of Clyst St. Laurance and Clyst-Gerard; in 1746 he surveyed the manor of Teign-Harvey; again in 1746 he surveyed five tenements in the parish of Bovey-Tracey; as well as tenements in Culliton, Newton Ferrers and Teignmouth. He also surveyed other properties for the Chamber in connection with charities in Awliscombe, Uffculm, Halberton, Sowton, Sidbury, Buckland Newton (in Dorset), Lyme Regis, and Exmouth. Most of these maps, together with those of his successor and others, are bound into a special 'Book of Vellum' ordered for the mapping of all the City Chamber's lands, estates and properties. The surveyor (i.e. John Richards) was to be paid £105 for the whole work or at the rate of 5s for each tenement in town and at the rate of 6s an acre for estates in the country. At the end of his appointment in 1760 he was paid £120, the balance of his bill. In the same year William Hayman was appointed as the Chamber's Surveyor with a salary of £35 per annum.[1]

Richards' surveys were bound together in what is known as the Exeter Chamber Map Book[:2]
*This Book contains a Sett of Maps, or Charts, of all the lands and Tenements belonging to the Chamber of Exon, situate within the City and County of the City of Exon and elsewhere; carefully Plann'd, and laid down, in their just Proportions, by the several Scales inserted in them respectively Together with written Descriptions of each particular Tenement and the Dimensions & Boundaries thereof.*[3]

The book contained some 28 maps of which the latest was dated 1786. Of these Map 19 is dated 1744, Map 20, 1746, and a reference in the Act Book notes that Richards was paid for a map of the Slow Tenement in 1739 (Map 23). All three pre-date his appointment, and within the *Reference Tables* others can be post-dated. All these maps contain lists of the property and their occupants at the time of drafting. They are all manuscript plans on parchment and coloured. It is assumed that all the early ones were surveyed (and drawn) by John Richards.

It is probably no coincidence that John Richards' surveys were completed just after John Rocque had drawn his large map of the City. Rocque was a well-respected surveyor of estates and was engaged in drawing a 24-sheet map of London at this time. He would hardly have begun his Exeter work without making contact with or obtaining permission from the Chamber, and they would surely have referred him to their own surveyor. It is also unlikely that Richards did not make contact with Rocque. Co-operation at some level is a distinct possibility.

The accuracy of Richards' own surveys suggest that they each took some considerable time in the first drafting. The similarity of style and the length of information on the tenancies also suggest a later completion and an execution by one draughtsman. Whether this is reflected in a passage of eleven years is doubtful but presumably the surveys should be dated to 1746 and their final drafting to 1757, when they were formulated to form the 'Book of Vellum'.

Maps 2-16 are supplementary to Map 1. They cover the city and the lands immediate to the walls in detail and to a larger scale. Map 17 is a plan of the river and is listed in the Appendix. Maps 18-23 & 28 show various properties in Devon, but not in Exeter, that belonged to the Chamber. Maps 24 & 25 show lands in St. Sidwell, Northernhay and Exland. Map 27 shows the run of pipes and audits.

---

[1] Taken from Richards' obituary in the *Exeter Flying Post* in 1878 and Ravenhill & Rowe (2002).
[2] The maps are listed in *Devon Maps and Map Makers* by Mary Ravenhill & Margery Rowe (2002) at page 184ff (Volume I).
[3] The book has collection number ECA Act Book 14,f,228A.

## Appendix C

## Henry Besley

Few local printers published extensively but the Besleys of Exeter could probably claim to have been one of the most prolific of local publishers. By the mid-1800s the family-run business had a long tradition stretching back almost half a century. Thomas Besley (Senior) was born in 1760 and had various business addresses as printer, bookseller and stationer or bookbinder: he is listed in various directories of the time at Southgate Street (1801 and 1811); at Holy Trinity (1803); and at Bell Hill, or more specifically at 76, Bell Hill, South Street (between 1816 and 1834). It must be assumed that Thomas was mainly a jobbing printer taking on contracts wherever possible and not taking on the extra responsibility for publishing.

Thomas and Jane had 6 children including Thomas Junior who also became a printer in Exeter; Robert, born 14th October 1794 (died 1876), a type founder in the firm of Thorowgood and Besley and who became Lord Mayor of London 1869-70; and Henry (baptised 15th June 1800 at Holy Trinity) who eventually became partner and successor to the family business. Thomas died on 27th October 1834 aged 74.

Thomas' eldest son, Thomas (Junior), was born in Exeter in 1790/1 and married Mary (also born in Exeter the same year). They had one son, Henry, who is thought to have died in 1853. Thomas, too, was also a printer and bookseller, as well as stationer and library proprietor (1823). About 1816 we find works printed and sold by either T Besley Senior or T Besley Junior, obviously to differentiate between the two businesses, with the latter printing and publishing books until roughly 1836 although his *Devonshire chronicle and Exeter news* paper ran until 1853.

However, it was Thomas Senior's younger son, Henry, who took over the business of his father. The company had already been trading as T Besley & Son according to directories of 1825 and 1828 and they were listed as T & H Besley in directories of 1828 and 1834. The imprint *Printed ... by T and H Besley* first appears approx. 1820 (e.g. Hyam Isaacs *Address to the Jews*). The company published directories as well as Devon, Cornwall, Somerset and Dorset sheet almanacs from 1828. Their first map of Exeter appeared in that year and was advertised in the *Exeter Flying Post* of 3rd July.

The map of Exeter that J Warren executed for Henry Besley (32) about 1845 for inclusion in the *Route Book of Devon* was probably brought up-to-date more frequently than any of the other maps and plans included here. As such it may be pertinent to include a summary of the main changes made throughout the map's life. The original map is described fully on page 66. The map was included in editions of the *Route Book* (RB), sections were extracted for special *Hand Books of Exeter* (HB), the map was issued as a folding map (FM), from 1878 it was included in issues of the *Post Office Directory* (PO) and also appeared in a guide produced for Thomas Worth, son of Thomas who had taken over Mol□s Coffee House and turned it into Worth's Art Gallery, *Worth's Guide to Exeter - The Cathedral Hand Book* (WG).

**1. 1845**    See page 64.

**2. 1854**    Directions to *Pince's Nursery* and *To Veitch's Nursery* added outside border.    RB.

**3. 1869**    Signature of J Warren removed. The South Western Railway added from northeast to Queen Street and St. David's stations necessitating removal of nursery and stream. *To Veitch's Nursery* erased. Public Hall added next to prison. Additional developments, e.g. in southeast and along Workhouse Lane.    HB, RB, FM.

By 1870 the title had been reduced to EXETER and only the Besley imprint remains. The London and South Western Railway is now shown with Queen Street Station but Longbrook has disappeared (presumably underground). Of particular note are the new and separated reservoirs and the considerable housing at Victoria Park, in Prospect Park, along Black Boy Road, beside Clifton Road, in College Park and Albert Terrace. The Free Cottages are shown and Larkbeare has reappeared. In the References the Albert Museum replaces the Episcopal Charity schools which are now moved to St. Michael's and The Queen's Hotel replaces the Star Inn.

**From** *Worth's Handbook to Exeter c. 1901.*

| | | |
|---|---|---|
| **4. 1877** | Title simply EXETER (20 mm below border). Becker's signature erased. | HB. |
| **5. 1877** | Rougemont Hotel replaces City Prison (site acquired by the Devon & Exeter Hotel Co. in 1875). A new note added *FREEHOLD LAND SOCIETY'S ESTATE*. | RB. |
| **6. 1878** | Becker signatures reinstated. Rougemont Hotel shows signs of erasure. | HB, PO. |

**6. 1878** By 1881 the map had been enlarged to 275 x 345 mm and although no scale is shown it is to the same scale as the previous Warren maps or 30 chains = 40 mm. The title is repositioned (top right), the scale bar and the References are removed and the imprint changed to read H.Besley & Son. The area covered is increased to the South to include Pince□s Nursery; to the West to include Foxhayes, to the North to include Pennsylvania Park and to the East to include most of Heavitree. Considerable additional housing is shown especially in St. Thomas and north of Tiverton Old Road. The Grammar school and Wonford Asylum are shown in Heavitree. The railway is taken to the Basin and Gas Works.

| | | |
|---|---|---|
| **7. 1882** | The note *FREEHOLD LAND SOCIETY□S ESTATE* is omitted. | PO. |

**8. 1883** From *c*.1883 the map was lithographically altered. Larger size: 310 x 370 mm. The title is now: EXETER AND SUBURBS. Imprint: *PRINTED & PUBLISHED BY H BESLEY & SON, SOUTH STREET, EXETER*. New imprint: *ENTERED AT STATIONERS' HALL*. A plain three line border; North point. Extends out to Exwick, St. Thomas and Wonford. Certain lettering is redone and places are retitled (HM Prison instead of County Gaol) etc.

For the 1883 edition of Besley's *Directory* the map with new title measured 272 x 307 mm. The plan now extends to Exwick, St. Thomas & Wonford. Certain lettering has been redone and places re-titled. The Directory map was again made slightly larger for the 1884 edition, but otherwise was little altered. PO.

| | | |
|---|---|---|
| **9. 1885** | Minor changes, e.g. St. Anne's Well Brewery deleted behind the Rougemont Hotel and Victoria Hall and a nursery added by Velwell Villas. Deletion of T.G. stations. | PO. |
| **10. 1886** | Minor changes, e.g."Field" markings deleted at Pennsylvania Park, Combs Farm deleted, Trews Weir added, Grammar School changed from L-shape structure to small buildings. | PO. |
| **11. 1889** | Minor changes, e.g. STREET becomes ST in imprint. Higher Barracks becomes Cavalry Barracks, New developments replace Polsloe House and Recreation Ground, changes to roads and buildings at the Devon C. Constabulary – New North Road. | PO. |
| **12. 1890** | Minor changes, e.g. title redrawn (more floral), STREET in imprint and many names show signs of re-engraving. The area at St. Thomas shows developments: Pince's name removed at nursery; county ground added; and Cowick Road added at Union Street with change in depiction of buildings. | PO[1]. |
| **13. 1901** | Imprint: *Printed & Published by Besley & Dalgleish*. Size now 300 x 375 mm. The plan remains much the same but a lot of the lettering has been altered even when the same wording is retained. New developments along Black Boy Road and a reference to the *Freehold Land Society's Building Estate* north of Prospect Park. Workhouse Lane is now Polsloe Road with two brick fields (Exeter Brick & Tile Co. founded 1899) and Polsloe Park is now built-up. Illustrated previous page. | HB, WG. |

---

[1] Although the *Directories* were published frequently not all of the copies seen contained a map, for example, Exeter WSL also has copies for 1894 and 1900 lacking the map.

# Index

## - A -

*A Handbook for Travellers* (1859 insert), 80
*A Handbook for Travellers in Devon & Cornwall*, 76
*A Handbook for Travellers in Devonshire*, 76, 84
*A Map of the Western Circuit of England*, 40
*A Pictorial and Descriptive Guide To Exeter*, 100
*A Topographical Dictionary of England*, 56
*Address to the Jews*, 104
*Adventure in Publishing* (History of Ward Lock), 92
*Adventures of Pizzaro*, 44
Agricultural Exhibition, 74
Alms houses, 36
American War of Independence, 14
*An account of the sieges of Exeter by John Hoker*, 96
*An Elizabethan Guild of the City of Exeter*, 102
*An Original Manuscript Of John Hooker*, 96
Andrews, P, 38
Angel & Co., 74
Anglo-Saxon occupation, 9
*Antiquities of the City of Exeter*, 11, 30
*Archaeological Journal*, 82
Archaeological Society, 82
Armada negotiations, 18
Arms on maps
    Bishop's Arms, 32, 36, 42, 44, 58
    City Arms, 22, 24, 26, 28, 30, 36, 42, 44, 58, 72
    Hooker family Arms, 22, 26
    Royal Arms, 22, 26
Avery and Weightron, 98

## - B -

Bacon, George Washington, 82
*Bacon's New Pocket Map of Devon*, 82
Baddeley, M J B, 88
*Baedeker* guide books, 88
*Baedeker's Guides to Great Britain*, 90
Baldwin, Cradock & Joy, 44
Baldwin, Robert, 40
Bartholomew, John, 84, 88
*Beauties of England and Wales*, 44
*Beauties of Wiltshire*, 44
Becker, F P, 64, 94
Beer, J C, 28
Bell, Andrew, 10
Besley, Henry, 19, 50, 64, 68, 92, 104
Besley, Thomas (senior and junior), 50, 104
*Besley's Directory of Exeter*, 64
Bevys, Richard, 26
Billing, John, 74
Birt, Samuel, 34
Bishop's Palace bird's eye view, 32, 34
Black, A & C, 68, 76, 84, 98
*Black's Guide to Devonshire*, 84, 98
Book of Vellum, 103
Boundaries Act, 52, 54, 56
Boundary Commission, 78
Boundary Reform, 52, 54, 56, 60, 78

Bounsall, W M, 48, 70
Bowden, James, 92
Bowling Greens, 36
Braun & Hogenberg, 24, 26, 48, 86, 90
Braun and Hogenberg derivatives, 102
Braun, Georg, 26
Brice, Andrew, 11, 18
Brigg Market (Leeds), 14
Bristol & Exeter Railway, 50
Bristol and Devon Railway Station, 64
*Britannia*, 48
*Britannia Magna*, 30
British Association - Advancement of Science, 18, 80
*British Atlas*, 44
British Library, 22
Britton, John, 44
Brown, R, 58
Bryer, F, 94
Bunny for Bunhay, 32
Bunnye for Bunhay, 34

## - C -

Camden, William, 24, 48
Campbell, Tony, 58
Carew, Sir Peter, 22
Cassell & Co., Ltd, 86, 94, 102
Cassell, Petter & Galpin, 82
*Catalogue of Bishops*, 11
Cathedral of St. Peter, 9
Caymox, Cornelius, 26
Chanter, J R, 86
Cholera, 66
Church Congress (1894), 18, 98
City Prison (cross shape), 72
*Civitates Orbis Terrarum*, 26
Church Congress, 18, 98
Cloth trade, 11, 14
Clothes burning, 66
Clowes, William & Sons, 62
Coal wharfs, 58
Colby, Thomas, 52
Coldridge (city planner), 52
Cole, Roger, 44
Coles, Joseph, 32
Colliver, R, 58
Commin, J G, 102
*Cornwall Illustrated*, 44
Cotton, William, 102
Countess Wear, 13
Covent Garden, 16
Crane seller, 22, 26
Creighton, Richard, 56
*Curiosities of Great Britain*, 44

**- D -**

Danish incursions, 9
*Das neu-beharnischte Grosz-Britannien*, 28
Dawson, Robert, 54, 60
Day & Son (lithographers), 70
De la Motte, P H, 70
Deeble, William, 58
Defoe, Daniel, 13, 14
Devon & Exeter Institute, 18
Devon Chamber of Agriculture, 18
*Devon Illustrated*, 44
*Directory and Gazetteer* (Billing), 74
*Directory of Devon* (White), 10
Dividers and scale bar, 22, 102
Domesday Survey, 9
Donn, Benjamin, 36, 40
Drew, Mary, 58
Duchy of Lancaster and Cornwall, 70
Duke of Bedford, 19
Dulau & Co., 88
Dunsford, Martin, 42
Dury, Andrew, 38
Dyer, John, 18
Dymond, Robert, 80

**- E -**

English Civil War, 10
Estate plans, 42, 52
Exeter & Yeovil railway line, 76
Exeter Blitz, 16, 98
Exeter buildings
    Albert Museum, 76, 80
    Alms Houses, 32
    Alphington House, 46
    Aqueduct to the city conduits, 44
    Athelstan's tower, 9, 70
    Atwell's Alms Houses, 64
    Bampfylde Court, 21
    Barn Field Brook Sewers, 62
    Bedford Chapel, 19
    Bedford Street Theatre, 86
    Bellair, 15
    Blackaller Wear, 14
    Blew Boys School, 40
    Blue Maid's Hospital, 34
    Bridwell or Brydewol, 26
    Broad Gate, 50
    Bude Hotel, 84
    Cattle Market, 68
    City Commercial Hotel, 84
    Coaver, 15
    County Bridewell, 32, 36, 50
    County Gaol (or Goal), 19, 46
    County Sessions House, 58
    Cowick Priory, 46
    Cowick Street Militia Barracks, 74
    Cricklepit Mill, 13
    Custom House, 13
    Deaf and Dumb Institute, 50

Deller's Cafe, 21
Devon & Exeter Hospital, 19, 90
Diocesan Trinity College, 84
Drill Hall, 88
Electricity Station, 16, 100
Electricity Works, 98
Episcopal Chapel (1832), 58
Exe Bridge, 19
Exeter Canal, 14, 16, 19
Fairpark, 80
Gas works, 20, 50, 58, 64
Great Conduit, 10, 20, 32
Guildhall, 15, 32, 34, 96
Half Moon Hotel, 18
Hall of the Vicars Choral, 21
Higher Market (Queen Street), 16, 20, 64
Higher Summerlands, 16
Hoopers Buildings, 46
inns, 10
James Meeting Place, 18
King John's bastion, 70
Knave of Clubs, 44
Larkbeare, 15, 22, 24, 26, 46
Lethbridge's Alms Houses, 32
Loggerheads (toll gate), 15
Longbrook Street Theatre, 88
Lower Market (Milk Street), 15, 20, 64
Lower Summerlands, 16
Manwayring's Houses, 70
Mol's Coffee House, 18, 104
Mount Pleasant inn, 44
Mount Radford, 15, 42, 50, 80
New Basin, 19, 50
New Canal, 44
New City Prison, 50
New City Reservoir, 58
New Goal for the County of Devon, 42
New North Road toll house, 15
New Theatre (Bedford Street), 42
New Theatre (Longbrook Street), 98, 100
Pople's New London Hotel, 84
Post Office (in High Street), 84
Quaker's Meeting House, 44, 50
Queen Street Station, 16, 98
Radford Place, 15, 22, 24, 26
Rockfield Works power station, 16
Rougemont Hotel, 74
Seven Stars Inn, 10
Ship Inn, 18
St. David's Railway Station, 16, 19, 68
St. Leonard's (church), 22, 24
St. John's Hospital, 44
St. John's Hospital or High School, 40
St. Karlet's Cross, 96
St. Mary's Chapel, 20
St. Peter's Conduit, 10
St. Thomas' station, 68
Taylors Hall, 18
Telegraph offices, 80
the Athenaeum, 58
the Bridewell, 32, 36
the Castle, 9, 20, 72

the Haven, 36
the New Bridge, 42
the Synagogue, 40
the Water Engine, 40
the Workhouse, 19, 46
Tuckers Hall, 15, 46
Topsham Barracks, 80
Topsham Road toll house, 15
Veitch's Nursery, 68, 76
Victoria Public Hall, 18, 80, 98
Watergate, 24
Waterbeer Street Theatre, 19, 38, 42
Wesleyan Chapel, 88
Wharfinger House, 13
White Hart inn, 66
White Lion Hotel, 84
Exeter Chamber Map Book, 103
*Exeter Flying Post*, 72, 104
*Exeter Guide and Itinerary* (H Besley), 50
Exeter Horse Fair, 52
*Exeter Itinerary And General Directory*, 50
Exeter Literary Society, 18
Exeter parishes, 10
Exeter Quay, 16, 24
Exeter streets
　Baring Place, 16
　Barn Field, 42, 44
　Barnfield Crescent, 16
　Barnfield Road, 52
　Bedford Crescent, 16
　Bedford Circus, 19, 42, 44
　Bridge Street, 44
　Bull Mead, 42, 44, 46
　Bury Meadows, 74
　Butcher's Row, 11
　Castle Precincts, 46
　Chichester Place, 16
　Colleton Crescent, 16, 44
　Combe Street, 24
　Cook Row, 32
　Dix's Field, 16, 50
　Ewings Lane (fatalities), 66
　Fore Street, 15, 66
　Fryers Hay, 42, 44
　Genny Street, 34
　Graves Street, 44
　Goldsmiths Street, 32
　High Street, 11, 32
　Key Lane, 32
　Little Britaine, 26
　Little Silver, 44
　Milk Street, 34
　New North Devon Road, 16, 52
　New North Road, 66
　New Road (Howells Lane), 42
　North Road, 50
　Northernhay Row, 50
　Pennsylvania Park, 15
　Pester Lane, 66
　Pound Lane, 50
　Queen Street, 15, 17, 50, 58, 66
　Rack Lane, 14, 32

Red Cow Village, 68
Rocks Lane (Coombes Street), 58
Smithen Street, 11
Southgate Street, 32
St. James Street, 32
St. Leonard's Road, 15
Stepcote Hill, 19, 82
the Shambles, 11, 32
Tiverton Road, 84
West Gate, 11
Withybridge toll gate, 15
Exeter weir, 13
Exeter's underground passages, 10
*Exmouth and its Neighbourhood* (Bounsall), 48, 70
Exwick Mill, 46
Eyre, George Edward, 78

- F -

Fairlove, Ichabod, 26, 32, 34
Fairs, 16
Featherstone & Co., 60, 72, 76
Featherstone, Jane, 72
Featherstone, Samuel, 72, 76
Featherstone, William Charleton, 72
Featherstone's Circulating Library, 76
*Featherstone's Exeter Times*, 72
Fiennes, Celia, 14
*Fifty-Six New and Acurate Maps* (Moll), 10
Fortibus, Countess Isabella de, 13
Foundries, 16
Fowler, Charles, 16, 20
Freeman, Edward, 13, 26, 90, 102
Freese, Daniel, 26
French Wars, 15
Fürst, Paulus, 28
Fullerton, Sir James, 70
Fulling Mill, 14

- G -

Galpin, Eliza, 92
Galpin, Thomas Dixon, 92
Gay, John, 10
General Fairfax, 10
*Gentleman's Magazine*, 40
German Luftwaffe, 20
Gilded leather screen, 102
Goad, Charles E, 92
Great Western Railway, 98
Greville, Fulke, 24
Grid system, 84, 88
*Guide to England and Wales*, 84
*Guide to Exeter and the Cathedral*, 104

- H -

Hackett, Thomas, 52, 54
Hackett, William, 52
Hall, Lt-Col. Lewis, 78
*Hand Books of Exeter*, 104

*Hand-book to South Devon*, 74
Hansard & Son, 52
Harcourt, William Vernon, 80
Harris, Sir Arthur, 20
Harte, William J, 96
Hayman, John, 44, 46
*Health of Towns*, 62
Hedgeland, P, 46
Hermannides, Rutgerus, 30
Hierat, Antonius, 26
*Historic Towns - Exeter* (Freeman), 90
*Historical Memoirs of Town and Parish of Tiverton*, 42
*History of the Norman Conquest*, 90
*History of Devonshire* (Moore), 58
*History of Exeter* (Freeman), 102
*History of Exeter* (Jenkins), 9, 46
*History of Plymouth* (Jewitt), 68
*History of the City of Exeter* (Oliver), 9
Hitler, Adolf, 20
Hoefnagel, Georg, 26
Hogenberg, Abrahamus, 26
Hogenberg, Frans (Francis), 26
Hogenberg, Remigius (Remy), 22, 26, 102
Hollar, Wenceslas, 68
Hooker, John, 9, 10, 22, 24, 26, 32, 48, 96, 102
Hooker, Robert, 22
Hooker's Ward, 60
Hooper, William, 16
Hunt, Rev. William, 90

**- I -**

Ikenild Way, 90
*Illustrated Handbook of Plymouth*, 68
*Illustrated London News*, 92
Inset map of Exeter, 24, 40, 82, 92, 94
*Insurance Plans for Exeter*, 92
*Intended Guyde for English Travailers*, 70
Iron age settlements, 9
Isaacs, Hyam, 104
*Itinerarium Curiosum*, 34
Izacke, Richard, 11, 30
Izacke, Samuel, 30, 34

**- J -**

James, Henry, 78
Jane, G, 30
Jefferys, Thomas, 40
Jenkins, Alexander, 9, 13, 46
Jennings, Robert, 58
Jewitt, Llewellynn, 68
Johnston (bookseller), 40
Johnston, J F W, 80

**- K -**

Kelly, Frederick Festus, 94
Kelly's Directories of Devon, 10
Kerslake, Thomas, 82
King Alfred, 9

King Athelstan, 9
King Canute, 9
King Edward the Confessor, 9
King Henry VII, 10
King James I, 70
King Sweyn, 9
King's Beam, 13

**- L -**

*La galérie Agreeable du monde*, 30
Lamb, Francis, 24
Lammas Fair, 16
le Keux, J H, 70
Lea, Philip, 24
Leland, John, 9, 70
Lewis, Samuel, 56
Lidstone, R (publisher), 68
Lieut.-Col. R K Dawson. *see* Dawson, Robert Kearsley
Lister, C B, 9
Liveing, Edward, 92
Lock. *see also* Ward, Lock & Co.
Lock, George, 92
Lock, George senior, 92
Longmans & Co., 90
Longmans, Green and & Co., 90
Lord Burghley, 102
Lübeck, 21
*Lundy Island*, 86
Lysons, Daniel, 26, 48, 68, 90, 102
Lysons, Samuel, 48

**- M -**

Maddock & Balderston (printers), 68
Madeley, G E, 55
*Magna Britannia* (Lysons), 48, 102
manuscript maps (Hooker), 22
March, John, 34
Marriott, Richard, 30
Marshall, William, 48
*Mathematical Essays*, 40
Meisner, Daniel (also Meissner), 28
Merchant Tailors Company, 24
Merian, Matthäus, 28, 30
Michell, John, 34
Moll, Hermann, 10
Moncrief, A R Hope, 98
Moreman, Dr, 22
*Moule's English Counties*, 58
Murch, Mrs (caterer), 68
Murray, John, 76, 80, 84
Musgrave, William, 32, 34
Mutlow, H, 48, 102

**- N -**

Nettleton, Edward, 68
*New Large Scale Ordnance Atlas - British Isles*, 82
Nicholls, Sutton, 11, 30, 32, 34
Nicholson, John, 10

Nightingale, Rev. J, 44
Norden, John, 9, 24, 70
Norman occupation, 9
Nosworthy, Matthew, 16

- O -

*Old Exeter Journal* (Brice), 11
Old Plan of Exeter, 86
Oliver, George, 9, 13, 20, 60, 70
Ordnance Survey, 52, 78, 92
Ortel, Abraham (Ortelius), 26
*Our Own Country*, 86, 102

- P -

Palmer & Stone, 74
Palmer, G G, 74
Paree for Paris Street, 32, 34
Parker, 34
Parker's Well toll gate, 15
Parsons, Capt. R M, 78
Petter, George William, 92
Philip, George & Son, 92, 100
Pim's paper mills, 46
*Plans of the Cities & Boroughs of England & Wales*, 52
Plymouth plan, 56
Pollard, Herbert, 98
Pollard, John, 72
Pollard, Thomas, 98
Pollard, William, 96, 98
Pollard, William & Co., Ltd, 96, 98
Pollard, William Carss, 72, 98
*Pollard's Official History and Guide to Exeter*, 98
*Post Mortem Vita* (Hooker motto), 22
*Post Office Directory* (Besley), 104
Post Office London Directory, 94
Powderham Castle, 13, 15
Prayer Book Rebellion, 10, 22
Price, Andrew, 22

- Q -

Queen Elizabeth I, 24
Queen Henrietta Maria, 19
Queen Victoria, 19

- R -

Rantzau, Heinrich, 26
Ravenhill, William, 102
Red Cow Turnpike, 52
Reform Act, 54, 56, 60
Reform Bill, 52, 54, 60
*Report Of The British Association 1869*, 80
*Report of the Commissioners* (boundary reform), 60
Reynolds, Herbert Edward, 96
Richards, John, 36, 103
Risdon (lithographers), 66
River Exe, 13
Robinson, E A & Co., 74

Rocque, John, 32, 36, 38, 40, 103
Rocque, Mary Anne, 38
Roman occupation, 9
Roper, John, 44
*Route Book of Devon*, 104
*Route Map*, 64
Rowe, Cornish & Hooper, 62
Rowe, Margery, 102
Royal Agricultural Show, 18, 68
Royal Agricultural Society of England, 68
Royal Society of Arts, 40

- S -

*Saint Richard*, 82
Sampson, John, 16
Saturday Review, 88
Saxton, Christopher, 22, 24
Schmollinger, Joseph, 58
Schmollinger, W, 58
*Sciagraphia Cosmica*, 28
Score, Edward, 32, 34
Serge market, 32
Serge racks, 34, 42, 44
Serpents (on map), 28
Shapter, Thomas, 62, 66
Sherwood, Robert, 32
Shitbrook, 64, 96
Shortt, W T P, 60
Sir Francis Drake, 18
Snail's Tower, 22
Society for the Encouragement of Arts, Manufactures
    and Commerce, 40
Soup kitchens, 66
South Devon Railway, 76
Soyer, M (caterer), 68
Speed, John, 24, 28, 30
Spottiswoode, William, 78
*Spreat's Churches*, 52
Sprint, John, 10
Standidge & Co., 62, 82
Stanford's Geographical Establishment 90
Street List, 72
Stukeley, William, 34
Sword and Cap of Maintenance, 10
*Sylva Antiqua Iscana*, 60

- T -

Tallis & Co., 44
Tallis, John & Co., 72
Taylors, Isaac, 40
*Telegraph* post coach, 16
*The Archaeological Journal*, 70
*The Beggar's Opera*, 10
*The Celt & Teuton in Exeter*□, 82
*The English Traveller*, 36
*The Flying Post* (Trewman), 11
*The Hand-Book of Exeter* (Jewitt), 68
*The Hand-Book to Exeter* (Palmer & Stone), 74
*The History of the Cholera in Exeter in 1832*, 66

*The Loyal Mercury* (Brice), 11
*The Official Guide to the London & South Western Railway*, 94
*The Postmaster* (Brice), 11
*The Remarkable Antiquities of the City of Exeter*, 34
*The Route Book Of Devon*, 64
*The Western Spy*, 72
*Theatrum Orbis Terrarum*, 26
*Thesaurus Philo-Politicus*, 28
Thorne, Nathaniel, 34
*Thorough Guide Series*, 88
Thorowgood and Besley, 104
*Times, The*, 88
Tiverton Gate (turnpike), 46
Toll-gates, 15
Toll houses, 15
*Topographia Germaniae*, 28
Topsham, 13
Tozer, Charles, 11, 42
Trade Guilds, 15
Tramcars, 16
Trewman, Robert
Tucking, 14
Turnpike gate at Parker's Well, 15, 44
Turnpike Trusts, 15
Turnpikes, 15

- V -

Van der Gucht (engraver), 34
Vicars (city planner), 52
Victoria Park, 64
*View of the Representative History of England*, 56
Vignettes, 36, 38, 58, 72, 74
Vincent, Alfred, 86
*Vincent's Guide to Exeter*, 86
Vowell, Robert, see Hooker, Robert
Vowler, John, 15
Voysey, Abraham, 103

- W -

Wage rates, 16
Walker & Boutall, 98
Walker, John & Charles, 56
Wallis, H J (publisher), 68
Warbeck, Perkin, 10
Ward, C S, 88
Ward, Ebenezer, 92
Ward, Lock & Co., 92
Ward, Lock & Co. Ltd, 100
Ward, Lock and Bowden Ltd., 92
Warren, J, 64
Water supply, 10
Waterside crane, 30
Wedgwood, Josiah, 68
Weekes, Miss Lega, 102
*Weekly Despatch* (Weller), 82
*Weekly Journal* (Brice), 11, 18
*Weekly Times Office*, 72
Weller, Edward, 76, 82, 84

West of England Engraving and Printing Office, 74
*Western Times*, 72
Wharfinger's House, 13
White, R, 36
Wilcocks, Mary Anne, 40
William of Orange, 19
William the Conqueror, 10
Wills, W, 52
Wind mill (incorrect), 30
Wood, John, 62
Wood, William, 74
Woollen industry, 14, 64
Woolnoth (engraver), 44
Worth, R N, 48
Worth, Thomas, 104
*Worth's Guide to Exeter,* 104

- Y -

Yeakell, Thomas, 42

- Z -

Zeiler, Martin, 28